C000231140

Great Inventions & Discoveries

A Concise Guide

Compiled by
John Geddes

Illustrations
Tim Archbold

NorthernBooks
from Famedram
www.northernbooks.co.uk

EUREKA!

COUCH POTATOES everywhere are probably aware that it is John Logie Baird of Helensburgh (page 6) they have to thank for giving them a screen to watch as they sit and snack. Sir Alexander Fleming (page 15) gets the credit for seeing the life saving qualities of a plate of mould and John MacAdam of Ayr (page 24) was responsible for giving us all that black stuff that now covers the country.

But what about James Chalmers of Arbroath (page 11)? John McLauchlin who emigrated to Toronto (page 23)? and James Nasmyth of Edinburgh (page 29)?

These lesser known heroes, to name but a very few, gave us, respectively: adhesive postage stamps (1834); *Canada Dry* (1890) and the steam hammer (1839), not to mention the pile driver and the dentist's drill!

The pages of this entertaining guide list many more mad – and not so mad – inventors from North of the Border who helped change the face of the world as we know it. It all adds up to a catalogue of the most amazing achievement.

THE INVENTORS

ANDERSON, Adam (?–d1846). Professor of Natural Philosophy at St Andrews. Contributed original papers on the measurement of the height of mountains by the barometer.

ANDERSON, James (1739–1808) of Hermiston, nr Edinburgh. Writer on political economy and agriculture. The inventor of the *Scotch Plough*.

ANDERSON, John (1726–96) of Roseneath, nr Dunfermline. Scientist. Author of *Institutes of Physics (1786)*. Creator of the *Balloon Post*. He also invented a gun which in 1791 he presented to the French National Convention

ANDERSON, Thomas (1819–74). Scottish organic chemist remembered for his discovery of Pyridine.

ARNOTT, Neil (1788–1897) of Arbroath. Became famous as a doctor and practical scientist. Prolific writer on natural science. Invented many useful appliances.

BAIN, Alexander (1810–77) of Watten, Caithness. Invented a chemical telegraph in 1843. He was also the inventor of an electric clock (1851) and a fire alarm system.

BAIRD, John Logie (1888–1946) of Helensburgh. The inventor in 1925–26 of television, which was first shown to the public in September 1929. Baird died while working on colour and stereoscopic (three dimensional) television systems.

BALFOUR, Sir Andrew (1873–1931) of Edinburgh. Novelist and expert on tropical medicine and public health. Made several important discoveries in protozoology.

BARR, Archibald (1855–1931) of Paisley. Engineer who with William Stroud founded the firm of Barr and Stroud, scientific instrument makers and pioneers in Naval range finders.

BARTHOLOMEW, John George (1860–1920) of Edinburgh. Map engraver and publisher. Best known for his system of layer colouring in contours.

BEILBY, Sir George Thomas (1850–1924) of Edinburgh. Industrial chemist. Improved the shale oil distillation and invented a manufacturing process for synthesising alkaline cyanides. He was elected a Fellow of the Royal Society.

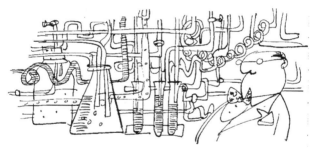

BELL, Alexander Graham (1847–1922) of Edinburgh. Went to America in 1870. Became professor of vocal physiology at Boston University in 1973. Best known for his invention of the telephone (1875–76). He also invented the photophone, a device for optically showing sound waves, invented a locator to detect metal objects in the human body, and produced the gramophone – an improvement on Edison's phonograph.

In 1918 he produced the HD-4 the fastest boat in the world; it reached a top speed of 70 mph (112 kph). Was a founder of the National Geographic Society.

BELL, Alexander Melville (1819–1905) of Edinburgh. Father of Alexander Graham. Teacher of elocution who invented and practised a system of invisible speech.

BELL, Sir Charles (1774–1842) of Edinburgh. Anatomist and surgeon. Discovered the functions of sensory and motor nerves. Facial paralysis, known as *Bell's palsy* is named after him.

BELL, Rev Patrick (1799–1869) of Arbroath. Invented a mechanical reaper in 1826. He did not patent his reaper and made no money out of it.

BLACK, Joseph (1728–1790) of Edinburgh. Chemist. He showed that the causticity of lime and the alkalies is due to the absence of fixed air (carbon dioxide) present in limestone and the carbonates of the alkalies. His fame rests chiefly on the theory of *Latent Heat* which he evolved.

BLAIR, Robert (?–d1828) of Murchiston, nr Edinburgh. Inventor of the fluid-filled achromatic lenses for telescopes.

BLANE, Sir Gilbert (1749–1834) of Blanfield, Ayrshire. Physician. Sailed with Rodney to the West Indies in 1779. As head of the Navy Board he was instrumental in introducing the use of citrus fruits on board ship to prevent scurvy.

BREWSTER, Sir David (1781–1868) of Jedburgh. Philosopher, physicist and inventor. Invented the kaleidoscope in 1816 and developed the stereoscope. Made important discoveries on the polarisation of light. *Brewster's Law* bears his name. He was founder of the British Association. Elected F R S.

BROWN, A B of Edinburgh. In 1870 he invented a servo-motor for hydraulic steering of ships by steam, air or oil.

BROWN, Robert (1773–1858) of Montrose. Botanist who discovered the nucleus of living cells. In 1805 he brought home about 4000 species of plants from Australia. Elected F R S in 1811.

BROWN, Thomas. Scottish engineer who in 1977 invented a computer linked 3D electric eye scanner for viewing inside the human body.

BRUCE, Sir David (1855–1931). Melbourn born Scot. Physician and naturalist. Discovered the causes of Malta fever and sleeping sickness. Elected F R S in 1884.

BUCHAN, Alexander (1829–1907) of Kinnesswood, nr Kinross. Meteorologist and pioneer of the Isobar system.

CAMERON, Charles of Glasgow. Chemist, who in 1820 invented apparatus for producing soda-water.

CAMPBELL, Angus. A Scot who in 1889 invented a spindle-type cotton-picking machine.

CHALMERS, James (1782–1853) of Arbroath. A bookseller in Dundee who invented adhesive postage stamps in 1834 – the round one penny stamp.

CLERK, Sir Dugald (1854–1932) of Glasgow. Inventor of the two-stroke motorcycle engine. He was director of the National Gas Engine Company, and director of engineering research for the Admiralty (1916).

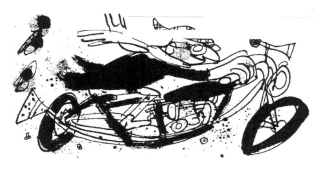

CLERK-MAXWELL, James (1831–79) of Galloway. Physicist. First professor of Experimental Physics at Cambridge (1871). Forecast possibility of radio transmission (1865). Invented Automatic Control Systems (1868). Creator of the electro-magnetic theory of light. Described as the father of modern science he was one of Scotland's greatest sons.

CULLEN, William (1710–90) of Hamilton. Physician to whom is largely due the recognition of the important part played by the nervous system in health and disease.

CURRAN, Sir Samuel C (1912–). Educated Wishaw and Cambridge. Principal, Royal College of Science and Technology, Glasgow (1959–). Chief scientist AWRE Aldermaston (1958–59). An authority on the detection of nuclear radiation. Invented the Scintillation Detector and the modern Proportional Counter.

CURRIE, James (1756–1805) of Dumfriesshire. Physician. Chief medical work was reporting on the effects of water on Fibril diseases (1797).

DAVIDSON, Robert (1804–99) of Aberdeen. Electrical Engineer sometime described as the father of the electric locomotive. Constructed two-person electric carriage (1839) and locomotive capable of drawing 5 tons at 5 mph in 1842.

DEWAR, Sir James (1842–1923) of Kincardine-on-Forth. Professor at Cambridge. Invented the vacuum flask, discovered cordite, jointly with Sir Frederick Abel. Liquefied and froze many gases including oxygen.

DRUMMOND, Thomas (1797–1866) of Edinburgh. Inventor, administrator and statesman. The inventor of *Limelight*. He was also head of the Boundry Commission under the Reform Bill.

DUNLOP, John Boyd (1840–1921) of Dreghorn, Ayrshire. Veterinary surgeon. He invented the pneumatic tyre in 1888.

ELPHINSTONE, Sir Keith (1864–1941) of Musselburgh. Engineer who between 1893 and 1914 was connected with the invention and development of many electrical and mechanical devices. He designed the first chart recorder, and invented the speedometer for motor cars.

ELPHINSTONE, William (1431–1514) of Glasgow? Statesman and lecturer on law in Paris and Orleans. Ambassador to France under James IV (1491). Was responsible for introducing the printing press (Chapman & Millar) into Scotland.

FAIRBAIRN, Sir William (1789–1874) of Kelso. Civil and mechanical engineer and inventor. First in the utilisation of iron for shipbuilding. Devised a riveting machine. He also built bridges (nearly 1000). Elected F R S in 1850.

FAIRLIE, Robert. Scottish engineer and inventor – in 1863 – of a railway engine with pivoted driving bogies, allowing trains to negotiate tighter bends.

FERGUSON, Patrick (1744–80) of Pitfour, Aberdeenshire. Inventor of a breech-loading rifle. In 1776 he patented his rifle which was capable of firing seven shots a minute and sighted for ranges 100 to 500 vards

FLEMING, Sir Alexander (1881–1955) of Darvel, Strathclyde. Bacteriologist. Discovered Penicillin in 1928. Elected F R S in 1943. Nobel Prize for medicine in 1945.

FLEMING, Sir Sandford (1827–1915) of Kirkcaldy. Canadian engineer. Took a prominent part in railway development in upper Canada. Chief engineer, Northern Railways (1855–63). He was the originator of *Standard Time*.

FORBES, James D (1809–68) of Edinburgh. Scientist and writer. Was one of the founders of the British Association in 1831. His investigations and discoveries embraced the subject of heat, light polarisation and especially glaciers.

FORBES, Sir John (1787–1861) of Cuttlebrae, Banffshire. Physician. Was joint editor of *Cyclopaedia of Practical Medicine* (1832–35). Translated Annenbrugger and Laennec and thus advocated use of the Stethoscope in this country.

FORSYTH, Alexander John (1768–1843) of Belhelvie, Aberdeenshire. Clergyman and inventor. In 1807 patented his application of the detonating principal in firearms, which was followed in 1808 by the adaption of the percussion cap. He was pensioned by the British Government after refusing to sell his secret to Napoleon.

GED, William (1690–1749) of Edinburgh. Printer and goldsmith. Invented a process of stereotyping in 1725.

GILL, Sir David (1843–1914) of Aberdeen. Astronomer to the Cape Observatory (1897–1907). Pioneered the use of photography as a means of charting the heavens.

GORDON, Sir Robert (1647–1704) of Gordonstoun. Inventor and reputed warlock. Designed a pump for raising water.

GREGORY, David (1661–1708) of Kinairdy, Perthshire. Mathematician. In 1691 became Savilian professor of Astronomy at Oxford. He it was who first suggested an achromatic combination of lenses.

GREGORY, James (1638–75) of Drumoak, Aberdeenshire. Mathematician and astronomer. A leading contributor to the discovery of the differential and integral calculus. Invented the reflector telescope.

GREGORY, James (1753–1821) of Aberdeen. Physician who gave his name to *Gregory's Mixture*.

HALL, Sir James (1761–1832) of Dunglass. Geologist. He sought to prove the geological theories of his friend and master (Hutton) in the laboratory, and so founded experimental geology.

HARRISON, James. Of Scottish descent, invented a refrigerator at a brewery in Bendigo, Australia in 1851. He later turned to the refrigeration of meat. In 1873 he gave a public banquet of meat that had been frozen in his ice factory.

HENRY, Joseph (1797–1878), born in America of Scottish parentage. Physicist. Made important discoveries on the subject of electro-magnetic induction.

The *Henry* (of induction) is named after him. In 1840 he became the first secretary and director of the Smithsonian Institute, Washington.

HILL, David Octavius (1802–70) of Perth. Landscape and portrait painter. The first to apply photography to portraiture.

HOLDEN, Sir Isaac (1807–97) of Hurlet, Renfrewshire. Mathematician and inventor. Studied chemistry in his leisure hours. Invented the *Lucifer* match, but was anticipated by John Walker of Stockton.

Holden was an associate of Lister.

HORSBURGH, Thomas. Scottish blacksmith who devised the first steel-shafted golf club in 1894.

HUTTON, James (1726–97) of Edinburgh. Geologist. The *Huttonian* theory, emphasising the igneous origin of many rocks and depreciating the assumption of other causes than those we see still at work, was expounded before the Royal Society of Edinburgh in *A Theory of the Earth* (1785). It formed the basis of modern geology.

ISAACS, Alick (1921–67) of Glasgow. Virologist and discoverer of Interferon in 1952.

KEILLER, Mrs Keiller of Dundee. The first to produce marmalade in 1797. Her son founded the Keiller Company, and marmalade became popular throughout the world.

KELVIN of LARGS (William Thomson) 1st Baron (1824–1907). Born in Belfast of Scots descent. Physicist, mathematician, philosopher, engineer, and inventor. Discovered the second law of thermodynamics.

Inventor of telegraphic and scientific instruments etc, including the improved mariner's compass and sounding equipment.

Elected F R S in 1851. Buried in Westminster Abbey.

Lord Kelvin's improved mariner's compass

KENNEDY, John (1769-1855) of
Kirkcudbrightshire. Cotton-spinner and inventor.
Introduced several ingenious improvements in the
spinning of fine yarns, including the *Jack frame*.

KERR, John (1824–1907) of Ardrossan. Physicist
and lecturer in mathematics. In 1876 he discovered
the *magneto–optic–effect* which was named after
him. He was the author of *An Elementary Treatise on
Rational Mechanics* (1867). Elected F R S.

LAIRD, John (1805–74) of Greenock. Shipbuilder. One of the earliest constructors of iron vessels.

LAPWORTH, Arthur (1892–1941) of Galashiels. Original chemist. Remembered for his enunciation of the electronic theory of organic clinical reactions in 1920.

Appointed to the Chair of Physical and Inorganic Chemistry in 1922. Elected F R S.

LEE, James Paris (1831–1904) of Hawick. Watchmaker.

Invented the remarkably efficient bolt-action and magazine of the Lee–Metford (later Lee-Enfield) rifle about 1890.

LEISHMAN, Sir William B (1896–1926) of Glasgow. Bacteriologist. Professor of Pathology in the Army Medical College and Director-General, Army Medical Service (1923).

He discovered an effective vaccine for inoculation against typhoid, and was first to discover the parasite disease Kala-azar.

LINDSAY, James Bowman. Invented the first electric light bulb in 1835 in Dundee.

LESLIE, Sir John (1766–1832) of Largo, Fife. Mathematician, natural philosopher and inventor. His many inventions include, a differential thermometer, Hygrometer, Photometer, Atometer and Althriscope. His researches appeared in 1804 in his *Experimental Inquiry into the Nature and Properties of Heat*. In 1804 he successfully applied the absorbent powers of sulphuric acid to freeze water under the receiver of the air pump. This is the first recorded achievement of artificial congelation.

LOW, Archibald Montgomery (1886–1956),
education, Skerry's College, Glasgow. Physicist
and inventor. His numerous inventions include a
system of radio signalling, a television system
(1914), electrical rocket control (1917), a coal-fuel
engine, radio torpedo control gear, the vibrometer
and audimeter. Was president of the British
Institute of Engineering Technology and of the
Institute of Patentees.

MacADAM, John Loudon (1756–1836) of Ayr.
Inventor of the *Macadamizing* system of road-
making commonly known as *Tarmac*. He was
appointed surveyor of Britain's roads in 1827.
MacAdam refused a Knighthood.

**MacARTHUR,   John
(1767–1834).**

A Scotsman who
became known as the
father of New South
Wales, Australia.

I n t r o d u c e d
sheep and planted the
first vineyard there in
1817.

MacEWEN, Sir William (1848-1924) of Rothesay. Surgeon. Founder of aseptic surgery and pioneer in surgery of the brain and lung, and in orthopaedic surgery.

MacKENZIE, Sir George S, (1780–1848). Mineralogist. First to obtain proof of the identity of diamond with carbon.

MacKENZIE, Sir James (1853–1925) of Stone, Perthshire. Physician. The inventor of the Polygraph to record graphically the heart's action. Elected F R S in 1915.

McLAUCHLIN, John. A Scottish chemist in Toronto. Invented the popular soft drink known as *Canada Dry* in 1890.

MacLEOD, John James Rickard (1876–1935) of Cluny, nr Dunkeld. Physiologist. Professor of Physiology at Cleveland, Ohio (1903–18), Toronto (1818–28).

Celebrated for his work on the isolation of insulin for which he won a Nobel prize. his father belonged to Wick, Caithness.

MacMILLAN, Kirkpatrick (1813–78) of Keir, Dumfriesshire. Blacksmith. Invented the first cycle to be propelled by cranks and peals (about 1840). A replica of his machine can be seen in the Science Museum, South Kensington. He was fined 5/- (the first recorded cycling fine) for knocking over a child. An unofficial dentist he also pulled teeth from both men and horses. He was known locally as *Daft Pate*.

McNAUGHT, John (1813–81) of Paisley. Engineer and inventor of the Compound Steam Engine.

MANSON, Sir Patrick (1844–1922) of Oldmeldrum. Physician who became known as the father of tropical medicine. The first, jointly with Sir Ronald Ross, to discover that parasites were transmitted by insects. He was sometimes known as *Mosquito Manson*.

MEIKLE, Andrew (1719–1811) from near Dunbar. A prolific inventor. Fantail gear (1750) and governing sails (1772) for windmills, a grain dressing machine (1768) and a drum threshing machine (1784) were but four of his inventions.

MELVILLE, Thomas (1726–53) of Glasgow. Scientist. Was the first (1752) to study the spectra of luminous gases.

MENZIES, Andrew. Scottish mining engineer. Invented a horse and man-powered coal-cutting machine in 1863.

MILLAR, Patrick (1731–1815) from near Dumfries. Inventor and projector of steam navigation.

MILLER, Maxwell of Glasgow. In 1850 invented an improved still for distilling and rectifying spirits.

MONCRIEFF, Sir Alexander (1829–1906) of Perthshire. Soldier and inventor. In 1868 he invented and developed the *Moncrieff Pit*, or *Disappearing System*. A method of mounting heavy guns in coastal batteries. The gun disappeared after firing and reappeared when required through the use of stored recoil energy.

MUNRO, Alexander (1733–1817) of Edinburgh. Anatomist. Wrote on the nervous system (1783), the physiology of fish (1785) and on the brain, eye and ear (1797). Was the first to describe the use of a stomach tube.

MORTON, Thomas (1781–1832). Scottish shipbuilder and inventor, (about 1822) of the patent slip which provided a cheap substitute for a dry-dock.

MURDOCK (originally Murdoch) William (1754–1839) of Bello Mill, Old Comnock. Miller and millwright. A prolific inventor. In 1785 he invented

a steam tricycle, gas lighting from coal (1796–1803), a steam cannon (1803), worm-driven cylinder-boring machine (1810) and a crown-saw boring machine. He also perfected underwater paint for ships.

MUIR, John (1838–1914) of Dunbar. Naturalist, explorer and inventor. He was also a conservationist who became known as the father of United States conservation. His inventions include a self-setting water-powered saw mill, various locks, hygrometers, clocks and pyrometers.

NAPIER, John (1550–1617) of Merchiston Castle, Edinburgh. Mathematician and the inventor of Logarithms (1614) and civil engineering devices.

NASMYTH, James (1808–90) of Edinburgh. Engineer and inventor of the steam hammer in 1839 and later a pile driver and a dentist's drill.

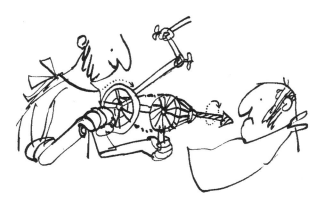

NEILSON, James Beaumont (1792–1865) of Shettleston. Engineer and inventor. In 1828 he patented his hot blast process, the technique of preheating the blast air in blast furnaces.

NICOL, William (c1768–1851). The Scottish inventor of the Nicol Prism which bears his name.

RAMSAY, Sir William (1852–1916) of Glasgow. Professor of Chemistry at Bristol (1880–87) and University College, London (1887–1912). In conjunction with Lord Rayleigh he discovered the gas Argon in 1894. Later he discovered Helium, Neon, Krypton and Xenon. He won a Nobel prize for Chemistry in 1904. Elected F R S in 1888.

RILEY, James of Glasgow. Engineer who invented nickel-steel in 1889.

ROPER, Andrew of Hawick. A farmer who in 1737 invented a winnowing machine.

ROSS, Sir Ronald (1857–1932). Born in Almora, India of Scottish parents. Physician who discovered – jointly with Patrick Manson – that malaria parasites were carried by mosquitoes and transmitted to their victims while sucking blood (1895–98).

RUSSEL, John Scott (1808–82) of Parkhead, Glasgow. Civil engineer and Naval architect. Invented the *wave system* of shipbuilding. He built the *Great Eastern* and other ships.

RUTHERFORD, Daniel (1749–1819) of Edinburgh. Physician and botanist. In 1772 published his discovery of the distinction between *noxious air* (nitrogen) and carbon dioxide. Subsequent study on the construction of natural gases was founded on his works. In 1794 he invented a maximum/minimum thermometer.

RUTHERFORD, Ernest (1871–1937). New Zealand born of Scottish descent. Physicist. Pioneer in atomic research. First to split the atom.

SHIRREFF, Patrick (1791–1876) of Haddington, East Lothian. Farmer who was a pioneer of cereal hybridising. He produced many varieties of wheat and oats.

SIMPSON, Sir James Young (1811–70) of Bathgate. Obstetrician and professor of midwifery. Discovered chloroform in 1847, having experimented on himself.

SINCLAIR, Daniel (Dane)(1852–1930) of Thrumster, Caithness. Telephone engineer and inventor of the telephone exchange. He was also the inventor of the hollow solder tube containing fluxite. In his day he was regarded as one of the leading telephone engineers in the world. He became chairman of several power distribution and telephone companies.

SINCLAIR, James, 14th Earl of Caithness (1824–81). He patented many ingenious inventions, including a loom, steam carriage and a gravitating compass.

SMITH, Adam (1723–90) of Kirkcaldy. Regarded as the father of modern economics. His book *The Wealth of Nations* was the product of the mind of the first systematic academic economist.

SMITH, James (1789–1850) of Deanston, Perthshire. Agricultural engineer and philanthropist. The inventor of *through drainage* by means of a subsoil plough (1823). He was the inventor of a rotary reaping machine in 1811.

STEVENSON, Robert (1772–1850) of Glasgow. Builder of lighthouses (including Bellrock). Invented the flashing system. Was also a consulting engineer for roads, bridges, harbours, canals and railways. He built 23 Scottish lighthouses. Robert Louis Stevenson was his grandson.

STEVENSON, Thomas (1818–87) of Edinburgh. Son of Robert. Joined with his father and brother

David in lighthouse construction and lighting methods in particular. He was the inventor of the thermometer screen, which is known by his name.

STIRLING, Rev Dr Robert (1790–1878) of Methven, Perthshire. Invented a type of gas-sealed internal combustion engine in 1817. His engine has been recently re-examined by British, Dutch and American engineers in connection with the development of a low pollution engine.

SYMINGTON, William (1763–1831) of Leadhills. Millwright and inventor. In 1787 he patented an engine for a road locomotive and in 1788 built one of the first steamboats. It had two paddle-wheels in the middle of the deck. He was also the inventor of a horizontal direct-acting engine which he patented and fitted in a tug called Charlotte Dundas in 1801–2. It was the first workable steam ship ever produced. He died in poverty in London.

TAIT, Peter Guthrie (1831–1901) of Dalkeith. Mathematician, physicist and philosopher. Professor of mathematics at Belfast (1854). Produced the first working thermo-electric diagram. Published many papers on scientific subjects.

TASSIE, James (1735–99) of Pollokshaws. Engraver and modeller. Famed for his paste and imitation gems. Was commissioned by Catherine the Great of Russia to supply her with some 15000 items of imitation gems and cameos. He invented the white enamel composition which he used for his medallion portraits.

TELFORD, Thomas (1757–1834) of Langholm. Son of a shepherd. A civil engineer who changed the face of Britain. Builder of bridges, aqueducts, canals and docks. The Menai Suspension Bridge was perhaps his greatest work (1825). Buried in Westminster Abbey.

TEMPLETON, James (1802–?) Scottish carpet manufacturer. Devised modification of Chenille velvet technique and applied it to the pile carpets and furnishings. Founded his Glasgow factory in 1839. Received several Royal Commissions from Queen Victoria for carpet. In 1850 licensed other carpet manufacturers to use his invention.

TENNANT, Charles (1768–1838) of Ochiltree, Ayrshire. Pioneer chemical industrialist. Developed and manufactured a bleaching powder.

THOMSON, James (1822–92). Scottish engineer born in Belfast. Brother of Lord Kelvin. He was an authority on hydraulics. Invented a turbine, discovered the effect of pressure upon the freezing-point of water and wrote papers on elastic fatigue, undercurrents and trade winds.

THOMSON, Sir Joseph John (1856–1940). Born near Manchester, son of a Scottish antiquarian bookseller. Physicist and discoverer of the Electron in 1897. Nobel prize winner for physics in 1906.

THOMSON, Robert William (1822–73) of Stonehaven. Civil engineer, inventor and expert on blasting. Designed and improved machine for making sugar in Java, invented a mobile crane, and in 1845, the first pneumatic tyre, but it was considered a curiosity and not developed, India rubber being very expensive at that time. He was also the inventor of a dry-dock and a fountain pen.

THOMSON, Thomas (1773–1852) of Crieff. Chemist. When making investigations in brewing and distillation, he invented the instrument known as *Allan's saccharometer.*

THOMSON, Thomas (1817–78) of Glasgow. Surgeon and naturalist. Discovered pectic acid in carrots.

TODD, Alexander R, 1st Baron Trumpington (1908–?) of Glasgow. Chemist and scientist, sometimes described as the most eminent Scottish scientist since Lord Kelvin. Has been honoured by the Russians for outstanding achievements in organic chemistry. Nobel Prize winner for research on vitamins B and E. Elected F R S in 1942.

URE, Andrew (1778–1851) of Glasgow. Chemist. Sometime Professor of Chemistry and Natural Philosophy at Anderson's College, and Analytical Chemist the the Bd of Customs, India (1834). He was the inventor of the Alkalimeter (1816) and a Bimetal Thermostat in 1830. Produced a *Dictionary of Chemistry* (1812). Elected F R S in 1822.

WALLACE, Alfred Russel (1823–1913). Born in Usk of Scottish descent. Architect, land surveyor and naturalist. Independently formulated the theory of natural selection before Darwin.

WATERSTON, John James (1811–83) of Edinburgh. Developed early kinetic theory of gases.

WATSON-WATT, Sir Robert Alexander (1892–1973) of Brechin. Physicist and inventor. Appointed Scientific Advisor to the Air Ministry in 1940. Invented and developed radar.

WATT, James (1736–1819) of Greenock. Mathematical instrument maker and prolific inventor. Developed the improved steam engine, invented the condenser (1765), sun and planet gears (1784), the governor, water gauge, parallel motion, smokeless furnace and a letter copying machine. The *watt* as a unit of electrical power is named after him.

WHYATT, Robert (1714–66) of Edinburgh. Neurologist who pioneered study of reflex action.

WILSON, Charles Thomson Rees (1869–1959) of Glencorse. Physicist. Pioneer in atomic and nuclear physics. Professor of Natural Philosophy at Cambridge (1923–34). Famous for his invention of the *Wilson Cloud Chamber,* an indispensable tool of modern physics ever since, and for which he was awarded a Nobel Prize for physics in 1927.

WILSON, Robert (1803–82) of Dunbar. Inventor of the screw propeller for ships, and in 1861 a double-acting steam hammer.

WILLIAMSON, John (1740–1803) (nicknamed *Johnnie Notions*) of Eshaness, Shetland. Weaver, blacksmith, carpenter and true pioneer in the fight against smallpox by serum inoculations. He was also a clock repairer and frequently dabbled in mechanical inventions, thus earning his nickname.

WOOD, Alexander (1817–84). Scottish physician who advocated the use of the hypodermic syringe for injections.

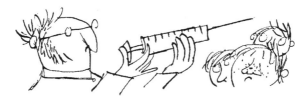

YOUNG, James (1811–89) of Glasgow. Scientist and founder of world's first commercial oil works (1851) after discovering a method of distilling oil from shale. Was sometime known as *Paraffin Young*. He was a great friend of David Livingstone, to whom he gave financial help, having amassed a large fortune. Elected F R S in 1873.

TERRITORIAL DISCOVERIES
By Explorers & Missionaries

BAIKIE, William Balfour (1825–64) of Kirkwall, Orkney. Surgeon, explorer, naturalist and linguist. Opened the navigation of the Niger. Constructed roads and founded a city state. Translated the Bible into several languages of Central Africa.

BRUCE, James (1730–94) of Kinnaird, Stirlingshire. Explorer in Africa. First to find the source of the Blue Nile. Discovered Tissisat Falls in 1770. His *Travels to Discover the Source of the Nile* (1790) was published in five volumes. Described as a formidable man, Bruce was 6'4" in height and strong in proportion. Had dark red hair and a very loud voice. He died as the result of tripping and falling down stairs when offering his hand to a lady.

CADELL, Francis (1822–79) of Cockenzie. Explorer in Australia. Explored the Murray River. Was murdered by his crew.

CLAPPERTON, Hugh (1788–1827) of Annan. Explorer in Africa. Died in his attempt to discover the source of the Nile.

COOK, Captain James (1728–79) born at Marton, Yorkshire, son of a Scottish (Roxburgh) farm labourer. Naval Officer, explorer and scientific navigator. Charted the east coast of Australia and named it New South Wales. He mapped much of the Southern Hemisphere and discovered the Sandwich (Hawaiian) islands where he was killed.

DOUGLAS, David (1798–1834) of Scone. Botanical traveller in North America. Discovered many new species of flora and introduced to Britain many trees and herbaceous plants, including the Douglas Fir which bears his name.

LAING, Alexander Gordon (1793–1826) of Edinburgh. Explorer. Served as naval officer in the West Indies for 7 years. Was sent to explore the Niger's source, which he found, but was murdered after leaving Timbuktu.

LANDSBOROUGH, William (1825–?) of Stevenston, Ayrshire. Explorer who with John McDouall Stuart was first to cross Australia in 1861–62.

LIVINGSTONE, David (1813–73) of Blantyre. Explorer and missionary in Africa. Discovered Zambesi river, Victoria Falls, Lakes Nyasa, Shirwa, Mweru, and Bangweulu. Buried in Westminster Abbey.

MacKAY, Alexander Morehead (1849–90) of Rhynie, Aberdeenshire. Engineer and pioneer missionary to Uganda (1878–87). Became known as *MacKay of Uganda*. Died of a fever at Usumbiro.

MacKAY, JAMES, Scottish botanist who discovered the sources of the Mississippi and Missouri rivers in 1784.

MacKENZIE, Sir Alexander (1764–1820) of Stornoway. Explorer and fur trader in N W Canada. The MacKenzie River which bears his name was discovered by him in 1789. He crossed the Rockies to the Pacific (1792–93).

MacKINNON, Quintin (?–d1892) of Argyll. Surveyor and explorer. Discovered MacKinnon's Pass in New Zealand about 1888.

PARK, Mungo (1771–1806) of Foulshiels, Selkirk. Botanist and explorer in Africa, and of the River Niger. Discovered the source of the Niger in 1796. Told of his adventures in *Travels in the Interior of Africa* (1799).

RAE, Dr John (1813–1893) of Stromness, Orkney. Explorer and Arctic traveller. Commanded an expedition (1853–54) to King William's Land. In 1854 he discovered the fate of the Franklin expedition, for which he was awarded £10,000. in 1860 he surveyed a telegraph line to America via Faroes and Iceland, and in 1864 surveyed a telegraph line from Winnipeg over the Rocky Mountains. He also mapped the north coast of Canada for the Hudson's Bay Company.

ROSS, Sir James Clark (1800–62) born in London of Wigtownshire forebears. Rear Admiral and explorer. Discovered the Ross sea which bears his name. He was also responsible, with his uncle, Sir John Ross, for the establishment of the true position of the magnetic north.

ROSS, Sir John (1777–1856) of Wigtownshire. Rear Admiral and explorer in Baffin Bay. Discovered the Boothia Peninsula in his search for the north west passage to the pole. With his nephew Sir James Clark Ross he established the true position of magnetic north. Was Consul at Stockholm (1839–46).

SELKIRK, Thomas Douglas, 5th Earl of (1771–1820). Explorer and coloniser. Settled emigrants from the Scottish Highlands in Prince Edward Island (1803) and Red River Valley, Manitoba. Became known as *Selkirk of Red River*.

SIMPSON, Sir George (1792–1860), Scottish Canadian explorer and administrator (1821–56) of Hudson Bay Company and its territory. Made an over-land journey around the world in 1828. Simpson's Falls and Cape George Simpson are named after him.

SIMPSON, Thomas (1808–40) of Dingwall. Explorer in the Canadian Arctic. Simpson Strait bears his name.

STUART, John McDouall (1815–66) of Dysart, Fife. Surveyor and explorer in Central Australia. Mount Stuart is named after him. With William Landsborough, the first men to cross Australia south to north (1861–62).

SUTHERLAND, Donald (1835–1919) of Wick, Caithness. Became known as *The Hermit of Milford Sound* in New Zealand. Discovered Sutherland Falls (one of the world's highest) which bears his name at Milford Sound. Sometime served in Italy with the forces of Garibaldi.

THOMSON, Joseph (1858–95) of Penpont, Dumfriesshire. Geologist and explorer in Tanganyika (1878–79) and Masai country (1883–84). The Thomson Gazell and Thomson Falls in Kenya are named after him. He explored Southern Morocco for the Geographic Society in 1888.

C000228372

THE LANCASHIRE CYCLEWAY

THE TOUR AND 17 DAY RIDES

About the Author

Jon Sparks is a photographer and writer based in Garstang. He has been a lover of cycling, especially cycling in Lancashire, for many years. His background includes riding road-races and hill-climbs very badly, and time-trials not quite so badly. More recently he has become a dedicated mountain biker and has also ridden a number of road sportives.

Jon is also a walker and (now very occasional) rock-climber and mountaineer. He is a member of the Outdoor Writers and Photographers Guild.

Other Cicerone guides by the author
Outdoor Photography (with Chiz Dakin)

THE LANCASHIRE CYCLEWAY

THE TOUR AND 17 DAY RIDES

by Jon Sparks

CICERONE

2 POLICE SQUARE, MILNTHORPE, CUMBRIA LA7 7PY
www.cicerone.co.uk

Second edition 2017
ISBN-13:978 1 85284 849 1

First edition 2003
ISBN-10:1 85284 384 5
ISBN-13:978 1 85284 384 7

Printed in China on behalf of Latitude Press Ltd
A catalogue record for this book is available from the British Library.

Route mapping by Lovell Johns www.lovelljohns.com.
All photographs are by the author unless otherwise stated.
© Crown copyright 2017 OS PU100012932.
NASA relief data courtesy of ESRI.

Updates to this Guide

While every effort is made by our authors to ensure the accuracy of guide-books as they go to print, changes can occur during the lifetime of an edition. Any updates that we know of for this guide will be on the Cicerone website (www.cicerone.co.uk/849/updates), so please check before planning your trip. We also advise that you check information about such things as transport, accommodation and shops locally. Even rights of way can be altered over time. We are always grateful for information about any discrepancies between a guidebook and the facts on the ground, sent by email to updates@cicerone.co.uk or by post to Cicerone, 2 Police Square, Milnthorpe LA7 7PY, United Kingdom.

Front cover: On Merrybent Hill (Northern Loop, Stage 2)

CONTENTS

Symbols used on route maps

	route	▲	peak
	alternative route	■	railway station
Ⓢ	start point		Area of Outstanding Natural Beauty, eg *Arnside and Silverdale*
Ⓕ	finish point		
ⓈⒻ	start/finish point		
<	direction of route		

Relief

	>1100m
	1000m
	900m
	800m
	700m
	600m
	500m
	400m
	300m
	200m
	100m

0 kilometres 2   4
0 miles   1   2
SCALE: 1:200,000

Contour lines are drawn at 50m intervals and labelled at 100m intervals.

Note: the maps for The Lancaster Link (Stage 1a) and The Wigan Link (Stage 9a) are at 1:100,000 scale.

GPX files
GPX files for all routes can be downloaded for free at www.cicerone.co.uk/849/GPX

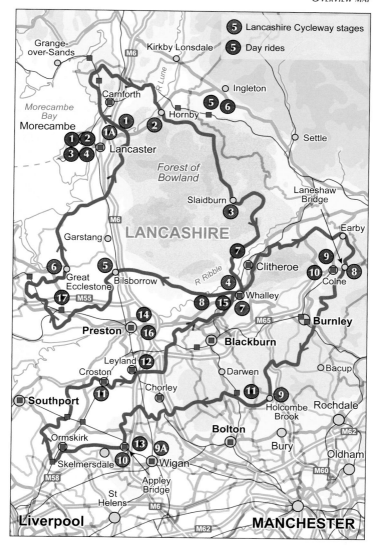

Legend:
- **5** Lancashire Cycleway stages
- **5** Day rides

Map labels:
Grange-over-Sands, Kirkby Lonsdale, M6, R Lune, Ingleton, Carnforth, Hornby, **5**, **6**, Settle, Morecambe Bay, **1**, **2**, Morecambe, **1**, **2**, **1A**, **3**, **4**, Lancaster, Forest of Bowland, Laneshaw Bridge, Slaidburn, **3**, Earby, LANCASHIRE, Garstang, **7**, **9**, **6**, Great Ecclestone, **5**, Bilsborrow, R Ribble, Clitheroe, **10**, Colne, **8**, **17**, M55, **4**, Whalley, **8**, **15**, **7**, M65, Burnley, **14**, Preston, **16**, Blackburn, Bacup, Leyland, **12**, Croston, Chorley, Darwen, **11**, **11**, **9**, Southport, Holcombe Brook, Rochdale, Ormskirk, **13**, Bolton, Bury, Oldham, M62, Skelmersdale, **10**, **9A**, Wigan, M58, Appley Bridge, St Helens, M6, M60, Liverpool, M62, MANCHESTER

Acknowledgements

I'd like to thank everyone I have ever ridden with. That's a long list, but I would particularly like to mention: my late parents, for many things, including having the good sense to move to Lancashire; Mike Thompson, for sharing the first steps into serious cycling; members of Cambridge University Cycling Club in the mid-70s; members of Lancaster Cycling Club and especially the 'Kellet Wheelers' from the late 70s to late 80s; and more recently Jonathan and Julia Westaway.

Various members of the Outdoor Writers and Photographers Guild have been eternally generous with those two vital commodities, information and inspiration.

I would also like to thank Alasdair Simpson of Lancaster County Council for large amounts of information and other assistance.

Last, and anything but least, I can never sufficiently express my gratitude to my partner Bernie Carter, for everything from pizza to proof-reading, and above all sharing great experiences, from New Zealand to Old Hutton.

Final stages of the climb of Farley Lane (Stage 11)

ROUTE SUMMARY TABLES

The Lancashire Cycleway					
Stage		**Start**	**Distance**	**Ascent**	**Page**
The Northern Loop					
1A	The Lancaster Link	Lancaster station SD 472 617	5.3km/ 3.3 miles	25m/80ft	34
1	Halton to Hornby	Bridge over River Lune SD 504 646	42.2km/ 26.2 miles	336m/ 1100ft	39
2	Hornby to Slaidburn	Main Street, Hornby SD 585 683	26.6km/ 16.5 miles	517m/ 1695ft	51
3	Slaidburn to Whalley	Slaidburn war memorial SD 712 524	28.1km/ 17.5 miles	218m/ 715ft	58
4	Whalley to Bilsborrow	Whalley station SD 729 365	29.2km/ 18.1 miles	155m/ 510ft	66
5	Bilsborrow to Great Eccleston	A6/Bilsborrow Lane junction SD 510 396	44.5km/ 27.7 miles	122m/ 400ft	71
6	Great Eccleston to Halton	High Street, Great Eccleston SD 426 403	37.9km/ 23.5 miles	149m/ 490ft	78
The Southern Loop					
7	Whalley to Laneshaw Bridge	Whalley station SD 729 365	37.3km/ 23.2 miles	648m/ 2125ft	89
8	Laneshaw Bridge to Holcombe Brook	A650/School Lane junction, Laneshaw Bridge SD 923 407	43.9km/ 27.3 miles	691m/ 2265ft	98
9	Holcombe Brook to Appley Bridge	Traffic lights, Holcombe Brook SD 780 153	43.6km/ 27.1 miles	470m/ 1540ft	107
9A	The Wigan Link	Wigan North Western station SD 581 054	8.4km/ 5.2 miles	Nil (actually negative!)	115
10	Appley Bridge to Croston	Canal bridge, Appley Bridge SD 523 093	49.7km/ 30.9 miles	176m/ 575ft	119
11	Croston to Whalley	Croston station SD 486 193	42.6km/ 26.5 miles	400m/ 1310ft	127

Day Rides						
Ride		Start	Finish (if not a circuit)	Distance	Ascent	Page
1	Lancaster–Silverdale one-way	Lancaster station SD 472 617	Silverdale station SD 476 751	22km/ 13.7 miles	140m/ 460ft	136
2	Lancaster–Silverdale–Lancaster	Lancaster station SD 472 617		54.5km/ 33.9 miles	478m/ 1570ft	138
3	Lancaster–High Bentham	Lancaster station SD 472 617	Bentham station SD 667 689	44km/ 27.4 miles	628m/ 2060ft	141
4	Lancaster–High Bentham–Lancaster	Lancaster station SD 472 617		74.1km/ 46 miles	855m/ 2805ft	144
5	High Bentham–Slaidburn–High Bentham	Bentham station SD 667 689		45.8km/ 28.4 miles	922m/ 3025ft	147
6	High Bentham–Long Preston	Bentham station SD 667 689	Long Preston station SD 833 579	34.5km/ 21.4 miles	648m/ 2125ft	151
7	Clitheroe–Slaidburn–Clitheroe	Clitheroe station SD 741 420		41km/ 25.5 miles	586m/ 1925ft	152
8	A circuit from Whalley	Whalley station SD 729 364		29.7km/ 18.5 miles	290m/ 950ft	154
9	A circuit from Colne	Colne station SD 881 398		47.4km/ 29.5 miles	1016m/ 3335ft	156

Day Rides

Ride	Start	Finish (if not a circuit)	Distance	Ascent	Page
10	Colne–Accrington	Colne station SD 881 398	Accrington station SD 757 285	38.7km/ 24 miles	685m/ 2245ft	158
11	Entwistle–Haslingden–Ramsbottom–Entwistle	Entwistle station SD 727 176		33.3km/ 20.7 miles	500m/ 1640ft	162
12	A circuit from Leyland	Leyland station SD 547 227		54.4km/ 33.8 miles	449m/ 1475ft	164
13	A West Lancashire circuit	Appley Bridge station SD 524 093		65.2km/ 40.5 miles	449m/ 1475ft	167
14	Preston–Whalley	Preston station SD 535 289	Whalley station SD 729 364	41.5km/ 25.8 miles	501m/ 1645ft	170
15	Whalley–Longridge–Whalley	Whalley station SD 729 364		34.5km/ 21.4 miles	409m/ 1340ft	173
16	Preston–Longridge–Woodplumpton–Preston	Preston station SD 535 289		50.4km/ 31.3 miles	264m/ 865ft	176
17	Kirkham–Lancaster	Kirkham station SD 418 326	Lancaster station SD 472 617	71.7km/ 44.5 miles	404m/ 1325ft	179

Waddington (Stage 3)

INTRODUCTION

Lune Valley from above Crook O'Lune, Ingleborough in the distance (Stage 6)

Cycling is one of the best ways of getting around, and of seeing places, that has ever been devised. It's fast enough to get somewhere, yet slow enough to see everything along the way. And you don't just see: you can use your other senses too. You can hear the birdsong and smell the flowers. Cars don't just travel too fast, they also insulate their occupants from the world outside – not least by creating noise and smells of their own. Cycling also means you feel the country: as Ernest Hemingway said, 'it is by riding a bicycle that you learn the contours of a country best, since you have to sweat up the hills and coast down them.'

Cycling is also immensely satisfying. To get somewhere by your own effort is rewarding in itself. And when you get to the top of a long hill, you'll appreciate the view all the more. But don't fall into the trap of thinking that it's all about suffering – it isn't. Cycling, above all, is fun. If you're sensibly prepared, if your bike is set up correctly for you (see 'Correct riding position' under 'Bike choice and setup' below), and if you don't try to go too far too soon, then cycling is one of the most physically pleasurable things you can legally do in public.

There are, then, plenty of good reasons to go cycling. But why cycling in Lancashire? This is easy to answer – Lancashire is beautiful. This may surprise a few people, but it's true. A few southerners may still cherish

13

the 'grim up north' image, but dark satanic mills, flat caps and whippets are generally thin on the ground. The plain fact is that most of Lancashire – especially as seen from the Cycleway – is rural. Indeed, it includes a lot of countryside that looks quintessentially English: rolling hills clad in a patchwork of fields, woods and hedges. But no such generalisation will do justice to the diversity of Lancashire.

Of course the county does have an industrial heritage. Two centuries ago, cotton was king and great mill towns like Blackburn and Burnley shipped cloth to half the world. The early days of canals and railways are well-represented too, not to mention Britain's first stretch of motorway. However, Lancashire's heritage goes much deeper. There are Roman sites like Ribchester, great mediaeval monuments like Lancaster's castle and Priory Church, magnificent houses like Stonyhurst or Samlesbury Hall, and literally hundreds of ancient villages. In a different dimension, Blackpool is the original seaside resort and remains, for millions, the definitive example.

Lancashire's rural character is particularly evident on the Northern Loop, but throughout the county green countryside is rarely far away. The Pennine moors offer vast expanses of open space, with the population largely confined to narrow valleys. Further west there are miles of level fields and reclaimed marshes, where you could almost imagine yourself in Holland.

The closeness of town and country is best exemplified where the Cycleway slips between Preston and Blackburn. Lancashire's two largest towns – correction, Preston is now officially a city – are barely 12km apart, yet the route finds quiet, shady lanes.

Further north, the population is concentrated close to the coast. Apart from Lancaster, which is not on the official route but is invaluable for access by rail, there are no large towns on the Northern Loop at all. Instead there is the gentle loveliness of the Ribble and Lune Valleys, flanking the high heathery ridges of the Bowland Fells. The county has sole claim on one Area of Outstanding Natural Beauty (Forest of Bowland) and a half-share in another (Arnside and Silverdale). The Northern Loop gives you a thorough look at both areas, while the Southern Loop makes brief acquaintance with the Forest of Bowland.

If you don't know Lancashire, it will surprise you. Even if you do, there are probably some corners you haven't yet discovered. Either way, cycling is a great way to explore the county.

THE LANCASHIRE CYCLEWAY

On a map the Lancashire Cycleway resembles a rather squashed figure 8, whose two loops meet at Whalley in the Ribble Valley. The Northern Loop is approximately 208km (130 miles) in length, the Southern a fraction longer at 217km (135 miles). There are similarities between the two, with both being

Descending from Cross O'Greet, Pendle Hill in the distance (Stage 2)

flat in the west and hilly in the east, but there are also distinct differences in character. The Northern Loop is almost entirely rural, while the Southern Loop, clever as it is, cannot entirely avoid some urban sections. None of these, however, are too long and, this being Lancashire, you generally soon escape back into open country.

The Northern Loop is entirely on tarmac. Apart from the (unofficial) Lancaster Link, which exploits a dedicated and well-surfaced cycle track, all of it is on public roads, mostly minor roads and quiet lanes.

The Southern Loop also has a few fairly short sections on surfaced cycle tracks, but otherwise the route again mainly follows quieter roads and lanes. There are a couple of urban sections, through Rawtenstall and Haslingden and also around

Adlington. Generally these are not excessively busy, but school run and peak commuting times are best avoided if possible.

This book describes both loops in a clockwise direction, but of course they can be tackled either way and are signed accordingly. At first sight doing the route anti-clockwise would seem to mean more left turns and fewer right turns. Left turns are easier when there's traffic about, which may be a consideration if you are nervous about tangling with cars. In fact, with such a complex route, there's little difference between the overall numbers of lefts and rights. Tackling the loops clockwise, however, takes greater advantage of the prevailing south-west wind for the flat sections, and generally means that the biggest climbs are taken from their easier side.

15

Experienced cycle tourists may tackle either loop in a weekend, or comfortably complete the entire Cycleway in a few days. The less experienced or less ambitious will be glad to know that it's easy to break it up into shorter sections: perhaps, but not necessarily, the eleven stages described in this guide. There is much to be said for the more leisurely approach, taking time to smell the flowers at the roadside, amble down to a river bank, or visit some of the attractions near the route.

Tackling the route as one (or two) continuous circuit(s) is only one approach. You can also break it up into day rides. The best way to do this is by using the trains (see 'Making connections', in Appendix B, for more details). The Southern Loop is criss-crossed by railway lines and

the permutations are almost infinite. The northern half of the county has a sparser, but still adequate, rail network. A selection of suggested day rides is briefly outlined after the main route description.

For reasons of space, further information concerning places the day rides pass through is not reproduced from the Lancashire Cycleway stage directions, but cross-references to the relevant stages are provided in the information boxes at the beginning of each day ride.

As the junction of the Northern and Southern Loops, Whalley is an obvious starting point, and the County Council has consistently promoted it as such. However, it is not particularly convenient for arrival by rail (from most directions). Visitors from outside the region will generally find

Whalley Abbey. Whalley is the hub where the Northern and Southern Loops meet (Stages 4 and 7)

Lancaster to be the best starting point for the Northern Loop, and therefore the description of the route starts here, but since it's broken into convenient sections, you can easily start from wherever suits you best.

For the Southern Loop, the choice is less clear cut. The route officially begins from Whalley, but again you can start anywhere that suits you: if you're arriving by rail the Wigan Link, connecting Wigan North Western station with the Cycleway, may come in handy (see Stage 9a).

If you're tackling both loops in one continuous ride you will transfer from one to the other at Whalley, but you can still start and finish at Lancaster, or anywhere else that suits you.

PREPARATION

Experienced cycle tourists can skip this section, but if your previous cycling experience has been confined to nipping out for a loaf of bread, or riding to school a decade or two ago, there may be several questions that concern you. The most basic, of course, is 'am I up to it?' And then there are other questions, like 'do I need a new bike?' and 'what do I need to take with me?'

Am I up to it?

For the majority of people the answer is yes, provided you prepare sensibly. Mind you, there's only one way to find out for sure! But tackling the Lancashire Cycleway isn't an all-or-nothing commitment. You can take it in easy stages, and many of them have bail-out options at railway stations. Pro cyclists might cover the Northern or Southern Loop in a few hours and regard it as a good training ride (one-day Classics like Milan–San Remo or the Tour of Flanders are significantly longer). Some experienced cycle tourists will happily tackle either loop in a weekend. But others may get equal or greater enjoyment and satisfaction from spending a week over one of the loops, or indeed doing it in dribs and drabs over a longer period.

Even 20km can seem a long way if you're not used to it. Like anything, cycling gets easier if you do it regularly, and as it principally uses the leg muscles – which are the largest in the body – it is among the best forms of exercise for all-round fitness. Using a bike to get to work or to the shops is a good way to get into the swing of cycling, as well as saving you money, and very often time as well. If that doesn't appeal or isn't practical, regular rides at evenings and weekends will do you good too.

BIKE CHOICE AND SETUP

Most bikes will serve. Maybe not the one buried in the garden shed, with wobbly wheels and rusty chain, but anything roadworthy will get you started. Of course, if your bike hasn't been used for a while – or maybe even if it has – it deserves a thorough check. If you're not sure of your mechanical

Daffodils near Wolf House Gallery, with Morecambe Bay behind (Stage 1)

skills, head to your local bike shop. A professional service will set you back a few quid, but it's worth it for the difference it can make, both to your safety and to your riding pleasure. If it gets you riding more often, the expense will be repaid many times over in petrol, car parking and other costs.

If you haven't got a usable bike already, it's well worth looking around for second-hand bargains. The boom in road cycling since the first edition of this guide means there are fewer road bikes languishing unused in sheds and garages, but bargains are still out there. Even if you have to replace a few components, excellent deals can be found, but be careful: if you aren't clued up about bikes, take advice from someone who is. Be particularly wary of bikes that appear far cheaper than they should be. Unscrupulous sellers may be keeping quiet about a hard-to-spot issue, like crash damage causing cracks or misalignment. And, of course, stolen bikes surface from time to time.

If you are buying a new bike – whether brand new, or just new to you – there are a few things to think about. A lot of Dutch people have several bikes, but most people in Britain manage with just one. As your new steed may have to serve multiple purposes, take time to consider exactly what you want to do with it before you open your wallet, preferably before you even start shopping around.

Despite the road bike boom, the majority of new bikes sold are hybrids. Hybrids look superficially like mountain bikes, with wide flat bars and fairly chunky wheels and frame. They're great for light off-road use, like canal towpaths or forest roads. True mountain bikes come into their own on rougher terrain, but if you're staying on tarmac, fat tyres and suspension will soak up not only the bumps, but also much of the effort you're expending. 'Supermarket special' mountain bikes – sometimes called 'bicycle-shaped objects' – are often excessively heavy, burdened with ineffective, essentially pointless suspension. For the Lancashire Cycleway, and pretty much everything else, they'll make your life worse rather than better.

For riding longer distances road bikes still have many advantages, not least that dropped handlebars give a greater variety of riding positions and allow you to be much more aerodynamic. This can become very important if you encounter a headwind on the Fylde.

The bikes used in the Tour de France may be feather-light works of engineering art, with carbon fibre frames and electronic gear shifting, but the essence of the design hasn't changed for well over 50 years. Bike-makers pursue innovation in the hope of selling more bikes, and there has been a steady process of development and upgrading, and the advent of ever more specialised and radical bikes, notably for time-trials and triathlons. Even so, the all-round

An endurance or sportive road bike is a good choice for riding long distances

bikes used for road stages in the Tour are still recognisably related to what Fausto Coppi or Eddy Merckx rode. This is, quite simply, because you can't improve on perfection.

Gorgeous though the Tour bikes may be, even if money's no object they aren't quite perfect for the Lancashire Cycleway. You're looking for something with a slightly softer and more stable ride, like the bikes now aimed at the sportive market. Sportives are mass-participation events, not races, over a range of distances up to, and occasionally exceeding, 100 miles.

A new, but very interesting, niche is the 'gravel' bike (terms like 'adventure bike' may be used instead). At first glance these closely resemble traditional road bikes, but they probably have disc brakes, have a slightly more resilient ride and are built to take wider tyres. They're still pretty nippy on the roads but can also handle off-road duties, well beyond mere towpaths and forest tracks.

In any case, budget at least £300 for a worthwhile new bike. If you plan to get serious, be prepared to invest significantly more. Cheaper bikes may look superficially similar but almost certainly won't last as long (or hold their re-sale value). If your budget is much below £300, you will be better off shopping around for a good second-hand machine.

Having said all that, any bike which gets used instead of bus or car will pay for itself sooner or later. If your employer is signed up to

Cyclescheme (www.cyclescheme.co.uk), you should be able to get tax breaks on any new bike up to £1000, saving you up to 42%.

Do you regularly get off and push on hills? A really vicious climb will have most people walking, but if you're regularly getting off on slopes of 15% or easier it's worth reviewing your bike's range of gears. With the right range of gears, cycling's easier than walking on any incline you'll meet on the Lancashire Cycleway (the maximum is about 18%).

If your bike's existing gears aren't low enough, it doesn't necessarily mean you need a new bike. New sprockets and/or chainrings may be all you need, with perhaps also a new rear derailleur – ask your bike shop.

If you do have a mountain bike, you'll almost certainly have low enough gearing for any climb on the Cycleway. For long days on tarmac, do yourself a huge favour and swap those knobbly tyres for something smoother. Those chunky knobs are for soft and loose surfaces; road tyres generally have pretty minimal tread. Higher pressures give a harder ride, but transmit your pedalling effort efficiently. However, current thinking is that wider tyres and proportionally lower pressures can give a smoother ride with minimal penalty in effort. For road bikes, 25mm to 28mm tyres have become much more common in recent years, even for racing. Mountain bikes and hybrids will have wider tyres anyway.

One other thing: traditional 'ladies' frame designs have little to recommend them, unless you actually plan to go riding wearing a long skirt. It's unlikely you'll want to do this on the Lancashire Cycleway, but if you're using the same bike for riding to work, then lots of bikes, including many contemporary road bikes, have a sloping top tube ('crossbar').

Correct riding position

Whether you're on a brand new bike or you've dusted off an old one, a vital and yet frequently neglected issue is getting the riding position right. Cycling might require effort at times – all exercise does – but it shouldn't be continuously uncomfortable, and there's no need to make it harder than it has to be. All too many give up after a few outings because their knees or back always hurt. It's simply tragic that so many people have never experienced the pleasure and sense of 'rightness' of a bike that's set up correctly for their individual dimensions.

A decent bike shop will be able to help you: in fact, if they don't take the time to fit your new bike to you, they aren't a decent bike shop. A real bike shop will also help you check your position on your existing bike. A basic assessment can be done in five minutes, and many bike shops will give you a quick once-over for no charge, especially if you're buying new tyres or other bits and pieces. However, if you're planning on riding far, or fast, or both, then the finer points of your riding position assume greater importance.

A full bike-fit is a serious and skilled business, and likely to take at least an hour. You can't expect that level of attention for nothing, but it's money well spent.

While a proper bike-fit requires skilled professional input, you can at least make a rough assessment for yourself. There are two essential elements.

First, get the saddle position right – not just height, but fore-and-aft as well. This is vital for efficient pedalling. Once it's right, you'll be able to ride faster for the same effort, or the same speed for less effort. A correctly set saddle also greatly reduces the risks of problems with your knees – usually when the saddle's too low, or hips – more likely when it's too high. The longer and harder you ride, the more important this becomes. As a very rough guide for saddle height, your leg should still be slightly flexed at the bottom of the pedal stroke. As a similarly rough check on the fore-and-aft position, set the cranks horizontal: you should then be able to drop a plumb line from kneecap to pedal spindle on your leading leg.

Second, get the handlebars set right. This affects stability, control, aerodynamics and above all comfort. Aches in the back, shoulders or neck (possibly all three!) are all too likely if this aspect is wrong. Again, both height and fore-and-aft placement need to be right. This may mean spending money on a new stem. Again, it will be worth it many times over.

If you find it impossible to get these elements even approximately

These riders both have an efficient but relaxed position on the bike

right, it may be that the bike itself, and specifically the frame, is the wrong size. If it is, no amount of fiddling with saddle and handlebars will make it completely right. With so many different frame designs now available, it isn't possible to give a short explanation of how to resolve this: consult your bike shop or one of the recommended books/websites listed in Appendix A.

With the riding position sorted, nothing can make or break your ride more decisively than the saddle. Choose one that's too hard and the results are obvious. But too soft a saddle can be just as bad. It may feel comfortable to sit on, but pedalling isn't sitting. There are many weird and (mostly) wonderful designs available nowadays, including cutaway types that may look like instruments of torture but actually relieve the pressure in crucial areas. Male and female anatomy differ significantly in these areas, and there is much to be said for gender-specific saddles. Saddle-fit is very personal, but is dictated above all by the spacing of your sit-bones (ischial tuberosities). This must be measured: you can't judge it by eye or infer it from other vital statistics.

<h2>CLOTHING</h2>

Having just discussed saddles, let's consider the bit that sits thereon. In warm weather shorts are great, but neither everyday nor running shorts are designed for cycling. Proper cycling shorts are cut for comfort when riding, and have padding in the crucial area. You can also buy padded inner-shorts which you can wear under ordinary trousers or tracksuit bottoms. Close-fitting, stretchy tracksuit bottoms are OK but baggy ones will catch on chains and gears and make your life a misery. In fact, baggy clothes in general will flap infuriatingly at speed and act like a sail when the wind's against you. Cycling shorts (or those padded inners) go next to the skin. Do not wear underwear beneath them: this grievous faux pas is potentially painful.

Shoes are equally important. A firm sole unit ensures that effort is transmitted to the pedals, and that the pedals don't feel like they're cutting into your feet after an hour or two. Trainers are not necessarily better than traditional shoes: it can be worth going through your wardrobe with an open mind. Cycling shoes are, of course, made specifically for the job. Out-and-out racing shoes can be difficult to walk in: mountain bike or touring shoes are better.

Old-style toe-clips and straps are now rare, as so-called clipless pedals have almost completely taken over. These greatly enhance pedalling efficiency, but must be matched with compatible cleats fixed to the shoes. There are many different cleat/pedal systems: Shimano's SPD is the best-known, but even this comes in two incompatible flavours; the 'mountain bike' variety is better if you plan on walking any distance.

For the upper body, dedicated cycling kit is great but can be pricey, and isn't entirely essential. There's no need to become a mobile advertising hoarding like the Tour riders, although bright colours make you more visible to other road users. A lot of cycling kit isn't vastly different from other outdoor clothing, except for being cut longer at the rear to avoid exposing the lower back when riding. Cycling jerseys often have rear pockets, a good place to carry essentials like wallet and phone, although not if you're also using a rucksack or bum-bag.

It can get pretty warm going up hills, and a lot cooler going down the other side. Traditionally, Tour de France riders would stuff a newspaper up the front of their jerseys for those long, chilly, Alpine descents. As newspapers aren't readily available at the top of Cross O'Greet, a light windproof layer is a good alternative for descents on cooler days. Although it rarely rains in Lancashire, it won't hurt if it's waterproof too.

Gloves have two main purposes: keeping your hands warm is only one. Proper cycling gloves have subtle padding where your hands rest on the bars, and this improves comfort immeasurably. In warmer weather, fingerless gloves with ventilated backs, often called track mitts, keep this comfort advantage but stay fairly cool. Some people, including some pros, can't bear riding with gloves, but I feel naked without them even on a two-minute spin to the corner shop.

Last but not least, a helmet may serve no purpose whatever most of the time, but there just might be that millisecond when it could save your life. Modern cycling helmets are extremely light and well-ventilated and you'll probably forget you're wearing one. If you still overheat, shaving your head has been found to help. Like everything else, a helmet must fit properly. Don't wear it tipped back on your head, as so many people do. The front rim should be, at most, three fingers' width above your eyebrows.

CARRYING GEAR

Weight is not the most crucial factor when cycling on the flat, but certainly makes a difference when you hit the hills. How you carry it is important too. A bum-bag is reasonable, but if you need to carry a large rucksack, think again. On your back is really the worst place for heavy loads. It will make your back sweaty, compromise your balance, and may obscure your vision to the rear. It can also give you backache and a sore posterior.

For day rides, especially if you buy food and drink along the way, you can travel very light anyway. A spare inner tube and/or patches, a multi-tool and a pump are vital, and you'll probably want a couple of bits of extra clothing in case the weather changes. This book is also essential, the relevant OS maps are a good thing too, and most people carry a camera of some sort. Incidentally, carrying a

Cycling is healthy, sociable and above all fun

A handy, adaptable saddle-pack from Apidura

repair kit is pointless unless you know what to do with it.

This much kit can usually be distributed under the saddle and in the back pockets of a cycling jersey or a bum-bag. A substantial saddle-pack is a traditional solution but a handlebar-bag makes everything just that bit more accessible. Some have a clear pocket on top to hold map or guidebook for instant reference (but don't read while you're riding!).

For trips involving a night or two away you'll need somewhat more clothing and a few toiletries. If you're crafty, and fairly strict about excluding non-essentials, you can still get everything into a good-sized saddle-bag or a saddlebag and bar-bag.

For longer trips, or if you're camping, panniers are the traditional way to carry substantial loads, but if you've never been cycle-touring before a trip that needs panniers seems a bit like going in at the deep end. On the other hand, if your bike already has a suitable rack, then panniers (maybe just one if you're travelling light) could be the easiest and most economical option.

POTHOLES AND PITFALLS

It has to be said: a lot of the roads on the Cycleway, like many others elsewhere in the county and across the country, have deteriorated noticeably since the first edition of this guide appeared.

As noted above, wider tyres run at slightly lower pressures will mitigate the discomfort of rough surfaces, but they won't help you if you hit a real pothole at speed. Keep your wits about you and scan well ahead for these hazards. Don't ride too close into the gutter as this can limit your options. If there's traffic about and you need to move out to avoid a pothole, make your intentions clear and make your move in good time.

DEVIATIONS FROM THE ROUTE

As this is an 'official' cycleway it's not up to a guidebook author to tinker with the route, but I have suggested one or two slight deviations where these seem to make sense.

There have been a few, mostly minor, modifications to the official route in the last decade. The most obvious is around Buckshaw Village (Stage 11 of the Southern Loop). What was a virtual wasteland when the first edition of this guide was published is now a large community, with hundreds of houses, shops, industry, even a new railway station.

One factor of growing importance is the spread of dedicated cycle routes, whether purpose-built or adapted. Where these provide traffic-free routes which link comfortably to the rest of the Cycleway, this is generally most welcome.

However, such provision can encourage the misguided (and thankfully rare) view that cyclists should only be on dedicated cycle tracks, not on the roads at all. When, and only when, cycle provision in this country is on a par with that in the Netherlands or Denmark, can there be any justification for such opinions. Meanwhile, and in the foreseeable future, we have every right to ride on all normal roads apart from motorways. Every time you or I make a journey by bike instead of by car, we are reducing congestion, not adding to it, for which any reasonable motorist can only be grateful.

Whatever the politics, there will be further changes to the Cycleway route in the future. It's even possible that a wholesale re-drawing of the route could take place, although this will only happen when funding is available to support a consultation process, new signage, mapping and so on. As author of this book, I hope to be involved in any such consultation and would welcome feedback from readers.

The obvious place to track such developments, you might think, is the internet, but I've yet to find a site that can be relied upon to be up to date. We'll do our best with the Updates tab on this book's page on the Cicerone website (www.cicerone.co.uk), and you can help by letting us know of any changes you notice.

SIGNAGE

Based on my experience (I re-rode the entire route in the early months of 2016), 99% of junctions on the Lancashire Cycleway are correctly signed. All well and good, but what

The Priory Church, one of the glories of Lancaster's Castle Hill (Stage 1a)

about the 1%, those odd spots where, perhaps as the result of mischief, signs are missing or wrongly aligned?

If you rely solely on signs to navigate, one missing sign (or even one that's momentarily hidden by a double-decker bus) can throw you right off, and by the time you realise you may have scant idea where you are or how to get back on route. It's wiser to maintain a running check against the text and maps in this book. GPS navigation is another great standby.

Several stretches are shared with other National Cycle Network routes and the proliferation of blue signs could be confusing. The Northern Loop of the Cycleway is NCN route 90 and the Southern Loop is route 91. Other NCN routes you'll encounter include National Route 6 (London–Cumbria), Route 55 (Ironbridge–Preston), the Way of the Roses (Route 69, Morecambe–Bridlington), and the Bay Cycleway (Route 700), unveiled in 2015, which runs from Walney Island to Glasson Dock.

Combined with the detailed route descriptions, the maps in this book should be more than adequate for navigation, but you may want to consider carrying Ordnance Survey maps as well as they give a much wider view of where you are and what you can see. As they show every road and track, you can also use them to plan alternative routes and links for future exploration of Lancashire. The 1:50,000 Landranger series is an ideal scale for cycling. To cover the entire Cycleway you'll need six of them:

• 97 Kendal & Morecambe
• 98 Wensleydale & Upper Wharfedale
• 102 Preston & Blackpool
• 103 Blackburn & Burnley
• 108 Liverpool
• 109 Manchester

The first four are needed for the Northern Loop; the last four for the Southern. Sheet 98 is only needed for about 10km of the route, with no complicated navigation, so you could well manage without: as it includes the final stages of the highest climb on the route, you may well feel that ignorance is bliss!

There are now many apps which allow you to access OS mapping

on a smartphone; check out www.viewranger.com for example. A good alternative to OS mapping is Open Cycle Map (www.opencyclemap.org). Alternatively, there's much to recommend a dedicated bike computer, which will allow you to keep your phone safely stowed, and conserve its battery. The simplest cycle computers cost little more than £10 while GPS-based ones start around £75. Most GPS computers can be used for navigation as well as for tracking rides, and many will display simplified maps as well as giving turn-by-turn directions. Garmin (www.garmin.com/en-GB) is by far the best-known name in this field; I've recently been using their Edge Touring Plus, which comes pre-loaded with maps of the UK and Europe.

Using any computer or tracking app will soon give you a sense of the average speed you can expect to achieve on a bike. This is a great help in planning your rides, as estimating times for cycling is notoriously more difficult than for walking. Walking speeds vary much less and there are many formulae and rules of thumb enabling you to work out how long a walk may take: Naismith's Rule is the best-known, if not necessarily the best.

Cycling speeds vary for many reasons; fitness, aerodynamics, the load you're packing, and so on. Hills will slow you down, but cyclists have much more chance than walkers of taking some time back on the descent – at least when there's a reasonable

Are there enough signs here?

surface and it's not too twisty. For example, the descent from Merrybent to Slaidburn at the end of Stage 2 is a good one; the descent from Marl Hill on Day Ride 7 is not (at least until they fix the road surfaces).

Still, even if your name is Chris Froome, average speed in the hills will be less than on the flat. If you're a bit more ordinary than Froomey, the time taken to cover a given distance may increase by up to 50% for the hillier stages; perhaps even more if you're heavily laden.

USING THIS GUIDE

This guide is divided into sections, averaging around 40 kilometres in length. The endpoints of these sections are either reasonable candidates for an overnight stop, or places with a train service, or often both. It's hoped that this structure will help in planning your trip around the Cycleway, but these are only suggestions and there are many alternative stopping-points.

Each chapter includes a detailed description of the route to be followed, accompanied by a route map, usually at 1:200,000 scale. In addition to the maps, there are route profiles for most stages. If there isn't one, you can assume that it it's flat!

At the start of each stage of the route you'll also find a box telling you:

- where the route description starts
- the total length of the stage
- the total ascent
- a brief outline of the nature of the actual riding (how hilly it is, how busy the roads are likely to be, and so on)
- the maximum gradient encountered (if this line is missing, the stage has no climbs of note)
- OS maps (Landranger sheets needed)
- an outline of train services on or near the route
- a general indication of where pubs, B&Bs and so on are plentiful and where they are thin on the ground: for more on accommodation, see Appendix A, Further information
- intermediate distances: cumulative distances of intermediate points from the stage start

Each stage is preceded by an introduction giving a brief sketch of the character, scenery and major points of interest of the stage, and the route descriptions mention places of refreshment along the way. It's a scientific fact that cyclists need lots of refreshment!

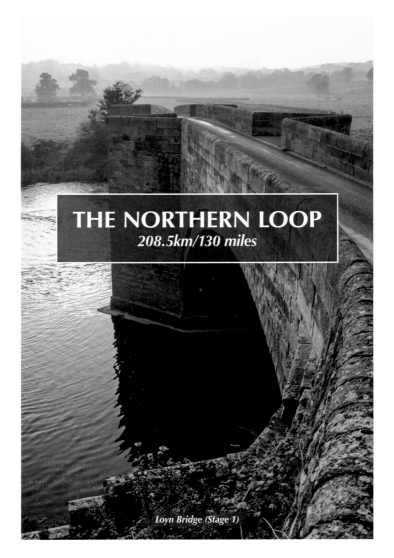

THE NORTHERN LOOP
208.5km/130 miles

Loyn Bridge (Stage 1)

INTRODUCTION

The Northern Loop embodies everything that's great about cycling in Lancashire. As a Tour de France stage it would be considered a moderate test, neither very long nor very mountainous, and would be knocked off in under six hours. However, if you would rather take six days over it, you will see more – a great deal more – and probably experience less pain and much more pleasure as a result.

As with any circular route, the first question is where to start. You might settle this by considering whether you would rather get the hilly part out of the way early on, or ease yourself in on the flatter stuff. However, if you are arriving by train, Lancaster is the logical starting place and gives you a fairly gentle introduction, then the major climbs, and finally a long, mostly easy winding-down. It's also historically appropriate, Lancaster being the traditional county town.

The Lancaster Link, following an old railway line out of the city alongside the River Lune, is a painless opening. You meet the official Cycleway route as you cross the river into Halton, the first of many attractive villages along the way. A short climb lifts you onto a ridge which gives prospects of things to come. You descend to Carnforth, then enter the Arnside and Silverdale Area of Outstanding Natural Beauty, the name nearly as

long as the area itself: this is the second-smallest mainland AONB.

Intricate and genuinely pretty, it may be small, but clichés about quarts and pint pots are almost irresistible. The often-leafy lanes twist and wriggle, and it would be easy to take a wrong turning, except that there are no wrong turnings here. However, if you follow the route as described, you'll get only the merest glimpse of the coast. It could be worth taking the short extra loop to Arnside (in Cumbria), which has a Youth Hostel as well as a great outlook over the Kent estuary.

The main route flirts with the Cumbrian border as it leaves the AONB, then crosses a corridor of flat country through which run the West Coast Main Line, Lancaster Canal and the M6. A quiet, undulating interlude charms its way across to the Lune Valley. There's a tucked-away feel to this patch of country, and some of the most traffic-free riding anywhere on the Cycleway.

As you sweep down into the Lune Valley, the great ridge of the Bowland Fells looms ahead. The climb begins soon after crossing the river, ascending by stages from wooded valleys, through more open pastures and out onto the wide moors.

A long steady climb, which gets steeper just when you least want it to,

Cross O'Greet is mean, moody – and magnificent. Not just for the views, either, sensational though they are. The climb itself – the actual business of getting up it on a bike – is genuinely challenging, perhaps all-consuming. But if you pace yourself, and your bike has the right gears, you can do it. And those views are infinitely better because you've got there by your own efforts.

Then there's the descent. Cooled yet elated, you swoop down into the warm little village of Slaidburn. Few things will ever taste better than that first pint at the Hark to Bounty or mug of tea at the café by the bridge.

From Slaidburn there's a bit more climbing, a mere bagatelle after Cross O'Greet, and then a grand section over a rumpled upland before you drop into the Ribble Valley. The local tourist office is fond of repeating that the Queen once said she'd like to retire to this area. One can see why: it encompasses a lot of proper English countryside, with small fields, hedgerows and a richness of trees, bounded by skylines of rock, peat, sedge and heather. Pretty villages – most of them not at all self-conscious about their prettiness – crop up at regular intervals.

At the heart of the valley is Clitheroe, one of the nicest small towns in England, clustered round a castle that surely never intimidated anyone. If Castle Street were traffic-free, Clitheroe would be just about perfect. As it is, maybe it's a good thing that the Cycleway sidles past just to the north. Then there's Whalley, with its serene Abbey ruins, and Ribchester, another handsome village and a significant Roman site.

In many other counties the next stage, looping at a discreet distance around Preston, would score pretty highly. By Lancashire standards it is merely pleasant. West of the main road and railway lines the undulations flatten out, the fields grow larger, and then reclaimed mosslands begin to reach to the horizon. On Rawcliffe and Pilling Mosses there's a dead flat, almost dead straight, run of 5km. It doesn't sound much, but compared to the ever-changing prospects more normal in Lancashire it seems almost endless.

If the wind is favourable (and it usually is) there's a fast run to Cockerham, where hills begin again. Gentle at first, the slopes get a little grander as the route hems the skirts of the Bowland Fells, through the Quernmore valley just east of Lancaster. Crook O'Lune is a lovely spot, and you may want to loiter a little. The fun's almost over, just that last, imperceptibly downhill ride back into Lancaster and the train.

Grim up North? You must be kidding.

STAGE 1A
The Lancaster Link

Start	Lancaster station SD 472 617
Distance	5.3km/3.3 miles
Total ascent	25m/80ft
Ride	Almost entirely off-road, but with better surfaces than many main roads and, apart from the optional climb onto Castle Hill, almost totally flat
OS maps	Landranger 97 Kendal & Morecambe
Connections	Lancaster station, West Coast Main Line
Accommodation	B&Bs and several hotels within easy reach. Lancaster's Tourist Information Centre is located in the Storey, a large building 150m down from the station on the main road (Meeting House Lane) towards the town centre: use the main station exit on the east side. The University of Cumbria's Lancaster campus (formerly St Martin's College) provides low-cost accommodation (student rooms) during the summer vacation.

This isn't officially part of the Lancashire Cycleway, but it's such a useful connection for those arriving by rail that it has to be included. Not only is Lancaster the nearest West Coast Main Line station to the Cycleway itself, but the connecting route out of town is almost entirely off-road (just 20m of back street to contend with), avoiding any tangles with traffic.

Lancaster is also the handsomest large town in the county (it's officially a city, but feels more like a town – and a good thing too). The only drawback is that it would be easy to be seduced into exploring Lancaster and forget about the rest of the Cycleway.

Leave the station through a gate alongside Platform 1. You may have to cross the footbridge (lifts available) to get there. To visit Castle Hill, turn left and left again, over the railway. To get straight into the Cycleway, turn right and follow the cycle path across a field.

Riverside view of Halton: a few steps from the route but screened by trees

Meet Long Marsh Lane, turn right under the railway and then immediately left on another cycle path, joining a former railway line. This runs below the Priory, through trees, then behind houses before emerging just above the river. Continue along the old railway line, past the back of Sainsbury's. Wiggle through an underpass beneath the busy Lancaster–Morecambe road. ▶

The underpass is ridable, given reasonable bike-handling skills, but the barriers could be tricky with panniers.

Continue past a small skate-park and under the road-way of Skerton Bridge. The imposing arches of the Lune Aqueduct are the next landmark. The next two bridges overhead carry a new link road and then the M6, after which you soon get glimpses of fine waterfront houses in **Halton**. Keep on to a small car park then turn left to cross the river on a narrow iron bridge. The official Cycleway route joins from the east here.

At the time of writing, the cycle path is re-routed around works on the new motorway junction/link road. Normal service may be resumed by the time this edition is published but, if not, the detour is obvious and easy to follow.

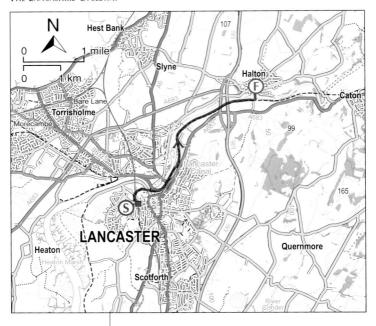

CASTLE HILL AND LANCASTER

This hilltop site, commanding the lowest feasible crossing of the River Lune, has been a strategic fortified site since Roman times, and may well have been occupied even earlier. Sporadic excavations, notably in the steep field north-west of the Priory, have yielded some evidence about Roman occupation, but the overall shape of the Roman fort and town is unclear: much must have been destroyed or covered by later buildings, especially the Castle. One small fragment of Roman masonry and the foundations of a bath house can be seen, but they will only excite the most dedicated antiquary.

The Castle we see today is built around a Norman keep, although its most distinctive feature is the 15th-century gatehouse. Although this is referred to locally as John O'Gaunt's Gate it was actually built for his son, Henry IV, and it's uncertain whether John O'Gaunt ever visited the town.

The Castle housed a prison for centuries, right up until 2011, and John O'Gaunt's Gate finally opened to the public in 2013. Access remains limited: you can walk into the courtyard and visit the new café, and guided tours will take you further. Tour highlights include the Shire Hall, with hundreds of heraldic shields around the walls; the Crown Court; the original dungeons; and the Drop Room, where many condemned prisoners spent their last moments. Among famous trials which took place here were those of the supposed Pendle Witches, of whom more when we get to Pendle (Stage 7). Castle Hill also boasts many fine 18th-century houses, dating from the time when Lancaster was a major port.

Next door to the Castle is the Priory Church. The church is always open – although you can't just wander round when there's a service in progress – and it is exceptionally beautiful. The bulk of the building is 15th century. A particular treasure are the mediaeval wooden choir stalls.

There's a fine view across the city from the top of the steps alongside the church. Prominent buildings include some 19th-century mills, the Town Hall, and St Peter's Roman Catholic Cathedral, but lording it over everything on the hilltop opposite is the Ashton Memorial. Variously described as 'England's grandest folly' and 'the Taj Mahal of the North', it was traditionally known locally just as 'T'Structure'. The white Portland stone building, completed in 1909, was built for Lord Ashton, formerly 'Lile Jimmy' Williamson, as a memorial to his wife. He made a fortune from linoleum and oilcloth and in the late 19th century was the undisputed overlord of the town. Today the memorial houses displays and exhibitions and there are superb views from its balconies – but it's a steep climb, and out of your way. Still, every passer-by wonders what it is, and now you know.

BY THE RIVER LUNE

The route runs behind St George's Quay, the core of the former Port of Lancaster. In the mid-18th century it was, briefly, the second port of the nation. Many warehouses survive, now converted to other, mainly residential uses. Recent additions are very much in keeping, so the whole Quay retains a distinctly Georgian appearance. The centrepiece is the beautiful Customs House, dating from 1764, which now houses the Maritime Museum.

Part of St George's Quay, with the Customs House on the left

Lancaster's prosperity in this period was inextricably linked with the slave trade. This is now acknowledged by a small memorial, on the right after the first access ramp of the Millennium Bridge.

Almost exactly on the line of Roman and mediaeval bridges, the Millennium Bridge is dedicated to pedestrians and cyclists. The crossing links to another cycleway (yet another former railway line) which leads to Morecambe.

After the underpass, the grassy area known as Green Ayre was the site of Lancaster's second railway station, closed and demolished in 1976. Just beyond is Skerton Bridge. Built in 1783, it was reputedly the first bridge of its size anywhere in the country to have a level roadway. The ride continues past the backs of several industrial estates. On the left are islands in the Lune, then the weirs which mark the upper limit of the tides. In winter you can usually spot cormorants here. Above the weir a broad and relatively straight reach of the river is popular with rowers.

The Lune Aqueduct dates from 1797 and carries the Lancaster Canal. Its construction was so expensive that the canal company was unable to build another bridge at Preston, which would have connected the Lancaster Canal to the national network. A connection was finally made in 2002 (Day Ride 16 visits this Ribble Link).

STAGE 1
Halton to Hornby

Start	Bridge over River Lune SD 504 646
Distance	42.2km/26.2 miles; Arnside Loop adds 5.4km/3.4 miles
Total ascent	336m/1100ft
Steepest climb	Approx 5% (Thrang Brow)
Ride	Mostly rolling lanes: a fairly steep climb out of Halton, and another at Thrang Brow. Elsewhere gradients are moderate. One footbridge, where you should defer to pedestrians.
OS maps	Landranger 97 Kendal & Morecambe
Connections	Regular trains to Manchester (airport), and Leeds and Barrow-in-Furness from Carnforth; for the West Coast Main Line, change at Lancaster. Silverdale and Arnside also have trains to Manchester and Barrow. Hornby's nearest station is at Wennington (Lancaster–Leeds line).
Accommodation	Pubs, hotels and B&Bs in Silverdale, and in Arnside, which also has a Youth Hostel. The area has several camping/caravan sites. Thereafter little until the Lune Valley, where Hornby has two comfortable pubs and some B&B accommodation.
Intermediate distances	Carnforth 9.2km/5.7 miles; Silverdale 17.2km/10.7 miles; Borwick 30.5km/19 miles; Arkholme 38km/23.6 miles.

From Halton, usefully tied into the Lancaster Link, the route climbs onto a ridge which offers some great views, especially over Morecambe Bay. After Carnforth the way winds through the gentle scenery of the Arnside and Silverdale AONB.

Arnside, across the county boundary in Cumbria, is a useful and very pleasant place to stop. The views across the Kent estuary to the Lakeland Fells are superb, too. It's easily reached by a short optional loop, adding 5.4km/3.4m, described where it leaves the main route.

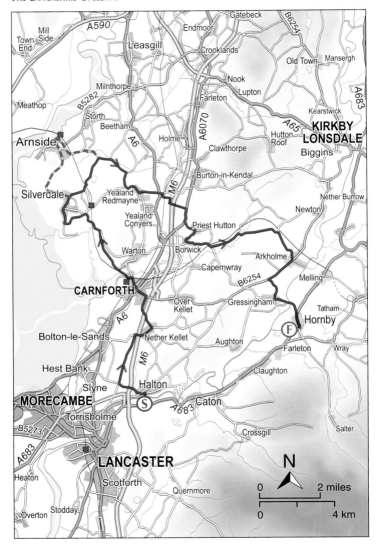

If you've come along the Lancaster Link, turn left. If you've ridden in from Crook O'Lune, turn right. Either way, cross the narrow bridge. The entry and exit show evidence of inaccurate driving, but there's additional space for bikes and pedestrians. Follow the lane up to a T junction and go left, passing the Greyhound Inn before rising to a mini-roundabout. Go straight across (second exit) into Foundry Lane.

Continue up through the trees then, still climbing, over the motorway to a crossroads. Turn right and climb steadily, passing a tall television mast. At the next T junction go right, re-crossing the motorway, then climb again through **Nether Kellet**. Near the top of the village turn left for Carnforth: you can freewheel almost all the way if you like.

> **Nether Kellet**'s village pub is the Limeburner's Arms, a highly appropriate name as there are still working quarries nearby. It's probably the most traditional pub on the Cycleway route. Don't expect food, and don't expect to find it open in the daytime either.

Turn left at a T junction onto the B6254 and go down into **Carnforth** over a narrow bridge with traffic lights, crossing the Lancaster Canal. Go straight ahead at the next set of traffic lights and down to pass Carnforth Station.

> Carnforth boasts one of the best second-hand bookshops in the north-west, and a variety of pubs and cafés. The main claim to fame is **Carnforth Station**, which was a principal location for one of

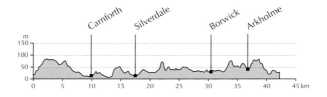

41

Carnforth Station, with its 'film-star' clock

the all-time classic British movies, *Brief Encounter* (released in 1945 and starring Celia Johnson and Trevor Howard). There's a pleasant tearoom (it lacks the smoky atmosphere of the film, which may be why it's pleasant) and some intriguing historical displays. The curved platforms that provided so many great camera angles have also been spruced up. Don't miss the platform clock, which figured significantly in the film.

Continue over one railway bridge (over the West Coast Main Line), then under a second (the line to Leeds). Turn left before a third bridge to follow a minor road alongside the muddy River Keer.

Pass under yet another railway (Furness Line), and a little further on cross the river by a fine wooden footbridge. At the end of the narrow lane turn right, go over the railway again, then left immediately on a wider road. This runs below the slopes of Warton Crag then over a level crossing. At the next T junction, turn left. After a short climb turn left again on Hollins Lane. The lane runs through woods, then descends to Wolf House Gallery.

Wolf House Gallery was established nearly 30 years ago, when craft centres were much thinner on the ground than they are now, and still retains a very high reputation. It is popular, however, and seats in the café may be hard to come by.

Follow the road round to the right, turn right at a T junction (Silverdale Hotel is a short way down to the left), then go up a short hump to another T junction. Go left here into the centre of **Silverdale**.

Silverdale village hall is named the Gaskell Hall after the great Victorian novelist, **Elizabeth Gaskell**, who spent many holidays here, usually staying at Tower House near Wolf House Gallery.

The road continues past the church, then dips and bends right.

Optional extra: Arnside Loop

Watch for a narrow lane on the left, by the war memorial. It's very easy to overshoot, but if you do, just take the next left – it will only cost you 100m or so. Assuming you found the lane by the war memorial, go left again at its end. The road leaves the village and trends right before crossing into Cumbria.

The road briefly skirts the shore then swings right at Far Arnside and drags up along the lower slopes of Arnside Knott. On the right are the ruins of Arnside Tower.

Striking **Arnside Tower** is a fine example of a pele tower. Peles – fortified manor-houses rather than full-grown castles – are scattered all over Cumbria and north Lancashire, areas which were often subject to raids from north of the border. You can take a closer look from the footpath behind the farm, but the ruins are officially unsafe to enter.

Almost opposite the Tower, there's a sign 'Footpath to Arnside'. In fact it's a bridleway and apart from the rocky passage of the first gate it's all

43

eminently rideable – a highly recommended detour if your bike is suitable. The track takes you over a shoulder of **Arnside Knott**, with sensational views over the Kent Estuary to the Lakeland skyline. The actual summit is only legally accessible on foot.

Higher up, the road has good views east. Beyond the lowland, the first abrupt ridge is Farleton Fell, and on the skyline beyond are the hills of the Yorkshire Dales National Park. From the final rise you can freewheel down to sea level again on Arnside Prom. However, if the youth hostel is your destination, beware of overshooting the turning – it's to the left before the final, steepest twist of the descent. To re-join the Cycleway route, continue along the prom and past the station. The road swings inland, keeping close to the railway before crossing it at a level crossing. Stick with this road until it ends at a T junction, then turn left. Here you re-join the official route.

Descending from Arnside Knott after taking the bridleway option

If you are not taking the Arnside Loop, continue straight on. The Woodlands Hotel, actually a quirky

old-fashioned pub, is up on the left. At the next T junction go left. The road now climbs a little, over the railway, then runs through woods. Down to the right you catch a few glimpses of a small tarn, Hawes Water. About 1km further on, on the right, is the entrance to Gait Barrows (see 'Nature Reserves' below).

The road bears right, past another junction, the northernmost point of the Cycleway, where the Arnside Loop re-joins at a junction with the Cumbria Cycleway. The road now runs along the little valley of Leighton Beck. After a short climb the road dips, swings right, and launches into the climb of Thrang Brow, which comes as a bit of a shock in this gentle scenery.

The road soon descends equally steeply, but watch out, as you have to give way at the bottom. Bear left, through Yealand Storrs and into **Yealand Redmayne**. Where the road narrows, go left on Eight Acre Lane, signed for Milnthorpe and Kendal. ▶ The lane, narrow in places, climbs over a small rise and drops to the A6.

The turning is hidden until the last moment.

Go straight across into Tarn Lane, pass Cinderbarrow picnic site (where a model railway offers rides on summer Sundays and bank holidays; donations requested) then turn right and first left. The lane crosses the West Coast Main Line then runs alongside the Lancaster Canal, with the M6 assaulting the senses just beyond.

The lane crosses the motorway and then the canal, climbs over a slight ridge, and descends to the A6070: go right. ▶ After about 800m turn off left, signed to **Priest Hutton**.

The road is wide and straight and traffic can move pretty fast, but there should be plenty of elbow room.

Keep right at the small village green and follow the lane towards **Borwick**, with its large green, backed by the grey stone pile of Borwick Hall.

> **Borwick Hall**, parts of which date back at least 600 years, is now a residential and outdoor centre belonging to Lancashire County Council. Say 'bor-rick', not 'borewick'.

Bear left, signed for Capernwray and Arkholme. After about 1km you cross over the railway line linking

Lancaster and Morecambe with Skipton and Leeds, which leaves the main line at Carnforth. ◄

Immediately after this bridge turn left. The road now runs parallel to the line in the valley of the River Keer (previously crossed just outside Carnforth). Follow the road as it swings right, away from the line, and begins to climb out of the valley. Descend to a T junction, turn right and follow the tiny valley of Beckerthwaite Beck. The railway line is once again in view. A slight climb gives more great views over the Lune valley before you swoop down into **Arkholme**. At the crossroads by the Bay Horse Inn, turn right on the B6254.

Arkholme is worth exploring. The main street (straight ahead at the crossroads) is long, lovely and blessedly quiet. At the far end the tiny church stands on an old motte and just below you can walk down to a tranquil reach of the River Lune.

Morecambe was a traditional holiday destination for West Yorkshire people, especially those from Bradford.

The valley of Beckerthwaite Beck, between Borwick and Arkholme

There's a steady, tree-shaded climb past Storrs Hall. Soon after this, turn left. The lane offers tantalising views before it slips down into the sheltered village of **Gressingham**. At a fork the official route goes right, but gains nothing by this slight detour. Go left instead, down to a T junction. Go left, and follow the road past the church and out onto the flood plain to cross the beautiful Loyn Bridge. ▶ Follow the lane to a junction with the A683. Keep right and freewheel down into the centre of **Hornby**.

This is uncomfortably narrow for modern traffic, though the milk wagon does just fit. The refuges above the bridge piers are welcome at times.

Loyn Bridge was seriously damaged in the floods of December 2015. Although it's been repaired and re-opened, there's still considerable evidence of the devastation around at the time of writing, including bent and twisted fences flanking the approach to the bridge.

VIEWS

This is a terrific stage for views, and if it comes at the start of your Cycleway journey, this makes it great for orientation too.

The climb out of Halton and over the motorway has the best view (from the official route) of the historic City of Lancaster, still dominated by its castle and Priory Church, although the domed Ashton Memorial on a higher hill east of the city contests the supremacy. Further east is the long purple skyline of the Bowland Fells, which you may view with either anticipation or dread. However, that's a good 60km ahead.

Before and after Nether Kellet there are views over Morecambe Bay, backed by the Lakeland Fells. The Coniston Fells, which lie further south than other high Lakeland hills, are particularly prominent. Coniston Old Man is about 45km away as the crow flies. Further right, although by no means the highest, the Langdale Pikes have the most distinctive outline.

On the approach to Arkholme there are fresh views to the east, over the middle reaches of the Lune valley. The distinctive squared-off hump of a hill which dominates the view is Ingleborough (of which more in the next stage).

HALTON

The manor of Halton is mentioned in the Domesday Book. It seems then to have been a more significant place than Lancaster, but the building of Lancaster Castle in the following century soon shifted the balance. You'll see several fine old houses as you come up to the mini-roundabout in the village, from which a short detour down to the left will reveal more of the old core of the village, including the pretty St Wilfrid's Church.

On your left as you climb Foundry Lane is a grassy hump, the remains of a motte-and-bailey fortress. This type of 'mini-castle', largely consisting of earthworks with the probable addition of a wooden palisade, typically dates from the Norman period. This is a very restricted site, overlooked by higher ground nearby – Lancaster is a far better strategic position.

A bigger and better example of a motte-and-bailey is Castle Stede, just above Loyn Bridge between Gressingham and Hornby. It's not surrounded by later buildings so it's easy to appreciate the layout. It's probably unnecessary to add that the nearby concrete pillbox is a much later addition.

NATURE RESERVES

There are several nature reserves in the Arnside and Silverdale area, the first to catch the eye being Warton Crag. The vast quarry, long disused, which scars the hill's southern flank, now attracts kestrels, peregrines and just a few especially brave rock-climbers. Above, on the hilltop, expert eyes have detected the outline of an Iron Age hill-fort, but the rest of us have to take it on faith.

Next comes the Leighton Moss RSPB reserve. Several fields near the road have recently been restored to reed-beds. There are a couple of hides accessed by a track on the left before the level crossing (to visit these you should be an RSPB member, or pay a day-charge at the centre). The main RSPB centre, which has a tearoom, is about 500m from the T junction after the level crossing – turn right, instead of left. However, this is a horrible junction for turning right – be very wary and use your ears.

Morecambe Bay and its hinterland are very important for migratory birds, especially waders, and huge flocks can be seen through the winter months. Leighton Moss has plenty of resident interest too. The three 'stars' are bittern, bearded tit, and – most spectacular, and most conspicuous – marsh harrier. In spring you may hear the bitterns 'booming', sounding rather like the sound you make by blowing across the top of a milk-bottle. While

One of the meres at Leighton Moss, with Farleton Knott on the skyline

often heard, sightings of bitterns are rare as they lurk shyly among the reeds. There are also otters here, and red, roe, and fallow deer are all found in the area. A grey rock face ahead of you beyond Silverdale is Trowbarrow Quarry, which was worked for limestone until the 1960s. Today it is a popular rock-climbing crag. Its unusual geology has earned it Site of Special Scientific Interest status, and it is also a local nature reserve (LNR).

Further on there's Gait Barrows, a national nature reserve (NNR); you can ride down the track a couple of hundred metres to a small parking area. Access is largely by permit only, but there are some way-marked walks open to all. A prime feature of Gait Barrows is its limestone pavements. It's easy to see why these are so called. Weathering of the relatively soluble limestone has enlarged natural fissure into deep cracks, known as grikes, which shelter a variety of ferns and flowers, but the upper surface is remarkably smooth. Parts of the reserve, and other sites in the area, have suffered from the plundering of the beautifully sculpted stone – branded as 'water-worn limestone' – for rockeries and other decorative uses.

The woods around Gait Barrows are typical of many in the AONB, with dark yew trees, a scattering of oak and ash, and lots of hazel around the edges and in any clearer patches. Most of the hazel bushes have multiple stems, the result of coppicing. This is the practice of cutting the tree back almost to ground level, which encourages it to put out a number of new shoots. Among other things, these were traditionally used for charcoal-making. One use for the charcoal would have been to fuel the nearby iron furnace.

ARNSIDE

Arnside is a thriving village in a superb location, and a great spot to spend the night – if you don't mind spending your money in Cumbria rather than Lancashire. If you fancy an evening stroll and don't want to plug up Arnside Knott, following the shore along to the west is a fair alternative.

The narrowing estuary of the River Kent funnels the incoming tides, and when conditions are right a distinct wave or 'bore' races up towards the railway viaduct. A siren sounds to warn of this.

Railway lovers should be aware that the crossing of that viaduct is one of the most scenic bits of line in England. It's 5km to Grange-over-Sands by train; 20km by road. You can also cross Morecambe Bay on foot: official cross-bay walks, led by Queen's Guide Cedric Robinson, start near the Albion pub on the prom, and finish at Kent's Bank station, the stop beyond Grange.

In its first incarnations, the Lancashire Cycleway continued a little further north into Arnside then worked across to Kirkby Lonsdale, all of which is actually in Cumbria, and is shared with the Cumbria Cycleway. Quite why the Lancashire Cycleway was ever routed through so much of another county may forever remain a mystery. The present route, although very close to the border in places, never strays across it. It's shorter than before and at least as good.

Anyone who has a train to catch, in either direction, should note that the station is a couple of minutes' ride from the village centre: just follow the prom and its continuation northward.

HORNBY

This substantial village, sometimes called the 'capital' of the Lune Valley, has two pubs and a tearoom. St Margaret's Church has an unusual octagonal tower which dates from the 16th century. The bridge over the River Wenning gives a theatrical view up to Hornby Castle. Most of the visible structure is 19th century, but some masonry below the tower is thought to be about six centuries older. It is a private house and not normally open to the public.

In the angle of the junction between the A683 and Station Road is a water trough, fed by a natural spring. On the wall above it a carved crest shows a cat which seems to have caught a rat. The story is that during the 19th century Hornby Castle stood empty for a while and became overrun with rats, and a large number of cats were needed to deal with them.

Station Road it may be, but there hasn't been a station here since 1968 – the site is now an industrial estate.

STAGE 2
Hornby to Slaidburn

Start	Main Street, Hornby SD 585 683
Distance	26.6km/16.5 miles
Total ascent	517m/1695ft
Steepest climb	Approx 15% (near top of Cross O'Greet)
Ride	Undulating minor lanes to start, then a major climb and descent
OS maps	Landranger 97 Kendal & Morecambe; 98 Wensleydale & Wharfedale (briefly); 103 Blackburn & Burnley
Connections	Early stages pass within 2–3km of stations at Wennington and Bentham (Lancaster–Leeds line); second half is the most remote section of the Cycleway.
Accommodation	Not much after Wray; a luxury B&B at the top of Merrybent Hill; Slaidburn has a Youth Hostel, a pub and a few B&Bs nearby.
Intermediate distances	Loftshaw Moss 11km/6.8m; Cross O'Greet 16.7km/10.4 miles; Merrybent 22.2km/13.8 miles

Don't be fooled by the modest distance: this is crunch time. Cross O'Greet, at 428m, is the highest point on the Cycleway. The exposed moorland roads can make it feel even higher on a bad day, but in clear weather the crossing is simply inspirational: the Yorkshire Dales, the Lakeland Fells and most of Lancashire seem to spread out around and behind you. And of course the descent is utterly exhilarating – provided your brakes are in order!

In really bad weather, soft options are hard to find. There is no handy low-level route to Slaidburn; the next road to the east, over Bowland Knotts, is equally high and exposed, while even the substantial detour via Giggleswick station, Rathmell and Wigglesworth (an extra 17km) tops out at around 265m.

At the southern end of **Hornby**'s main street, where the main road bends sharp right, go straight on (Station Road). Follow the road over the disused railway to the crossroads at Butt Yeats. Go left here on the B6480 for about 1.5km

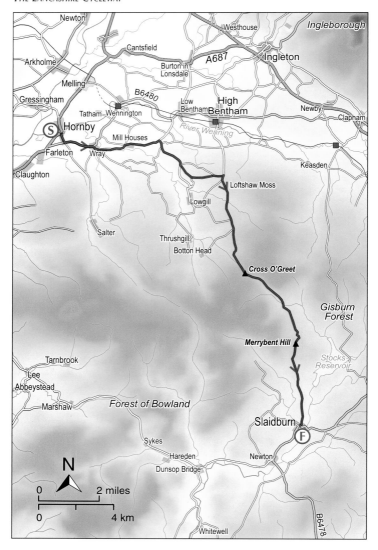

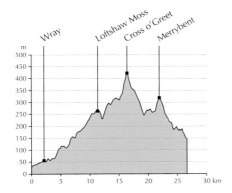

to **Wray**. Turn right down the main street, which swings left then down to cross the River Roeburn. ▸

After a level run above the River Hindburn, drop down again to cross it. Follow the road round left and right at **Mill Houses** before a sharp climb. The road then follows the spine of a little ridge, giving good views both ways, until it broadens out.

Bridge House Farm tearoom (recommended) is the last refreshment stop before Slaidburn.

Looking down to the Hindburn valley, with Caton Moor beyond

53

Go right at the next junction, signed for Lowgill, and climb steadily for 1km. There's a slight dip and then the road climbs again. Where it starts to slant off down right into Lowgill, there's a triple junction. Keep straight ahead, signed to Slaidburn and Burnmoor. The lane eases round above the Hindburn valley, almost level at first then climbing gently before reaching open moorland near Loftshaw Moss.

Visible to your left as you approach the T junction is a huge isolated boulder known as the **Great Stone of Fourstones** (there's no sign of the other three today). It's a fine viewpoint, easily climbed by carved steps.

At a T junction, with a great view ahead to the Three Peaks, turn right. The road climbs a little more then levels off, and you can assess the prospects for the rest of the climb. The road disappears in places in creases of the moor, but the final stage can be seen climbing to the lowest point of the skyline.

A bit of respite before the final stage of the climb

There's a brief downhill section before the road climbs again, still not too steeply. The sprawling Burn Moor obscures the view to the east now, but any time you

need an excuse for a breather, there remains a sweeping prospect behind you, over the Lune Valley to the Lakeland Fells.

The road dives into another little dip then swings right. The final stage is just around the next left-hander, out of sight but hardly out of mind. If you've studied the OS map you'll have noticed the menacing presence of a couple of arrows on the last kilometre, indicating gradients of 14–20%. It's probably towards the easier end of the range, but feels harder as you've already climbed, in total, more than 400m since Wray.

Reaching the top of **Cross O'Greet** will probably provoke some mix of triumph and sheer relief.

> There's no cross today at **Cross O'Greet**, but you can see its (presumed) former socket in a boulder at the top. Of greater interest may be the fact that this rock provides the only seating. The view ahead is narrower, a long wild valley, a wedge of lower hills, and the blunt profile of Pendle Hill.
>
> There's no real shelter up here, and on less than benign days it's easy to get cold. But at least take a quick drink and one last look back; it'll be a while before you see the Lakeland skyline again.

The first stage of the descent mirrors the last of the ascent, complete with warning arrows on the map. It twists sharply down across boulder-strewn slopes which fall away on the right to the valley of the River Hodder.

Soon the road straightens and the gradient eases. It's easy, at least on a decent road bike, to reach speeds of 60kph and more down here, but there are still bends, some sharper than they look. ▸

The final drop to the river and Cross O'Greet Bridge is open and fairly straight. While you might want to carry speed into the ensuing sharp climb through the plantation, be wary: the road surface around the bridge and under the trees is currently extremely poor.

Sheep can be a hazard, too, but excessive caution can mean missing out on the sheer exhilaration of this magnificent descent.

There's a relatively level stretch, a little dip at the crossing of Hare Clough Beck – a quintessentially Bowland name – and then the climb to **Merrybent Hill**.

> **Merrybent Hill** may be over a hundred metres lower than Cross O'Greet, but the view south and east is far more extensive. Pendle Hill stands in splendid isolation, while further east the land rolls down to the broad valley of Ribblesdale, backed by the long Pennine skyline.

If your legs have recovered from Cross O'Greet, this will seem trivial by comparison. But perhaps that's a big 'if'. Merrybent ushers in another grand descent, less technical than the previous one but potentially even faster. Just don't go so fast you miss the views, especially into Croasdale down on the right.

Over the bridge and into **Slaidburn**, the last rise considerably placed to slow you down without excessive wear on the brake blocks. At the T junction by the war memorial the onward route goes left, and the tea-shop's just around the next bend. However, the village shop, youth hostel and pub are all just up to the right.

WRAY

Wray is a compact village, its main street lined with stone-built cottages. In recent years Wray has achieved renown for its annual Scarecrow Festival, usually concluding with a fair at the May bank holiday.

The River Hindburn is no more than 15km long, but a lot of high moorland drains into it and it can be fierce after heavy rain, the 1967 floods in Wray being the best-known instance. They're commemorated in a mosaic, in the green area just before the bridge, which occupies the site of a terrace of houses destroyed by the flood.

Wray's Scarecrow Festival takes place around the May bank holiday

INGLEBOROUGH AND THE THREE PEAKS

Though a modest 723m, Ingleborough's position and distinctive outline give it great presence. It's the best-known hill in Yorkshire: the word 'iconic' comes to mind. From almost anywhere in the Lune Valley (Crook O'Lune, for instance, also on the Cycleway) it appears commanding, and it's easy to understand how some early map-makers estimated its height at nearly twice the true figure. Whernside, to its left, although slightly higher (736m), lies further back and appears far less imposing. The third of Yorkshire's Three Peaks, Pen-y-Ghent (694m), lies dead ahead as you approach the T junction on Loftshaw Moss, but also plays a supporting role to the bombastic Ingleborough.

An annual cyclo-cross race visits all three summits in its 61km course, with 1524m of climbing. Over half the distance is off-road and at least 6km are considered unrideable, yet the winning time is usually under 3hrs.

THE FOREST OF BOWLAND

The name Forest of Bowland uses 'forest' in its old sense, indicating a hunting preserve, not necessarily a wooded area. Gisburn Forest – seen from the climb to Merrybent – is atypical of the mostly bare Bowland landscape. It's now a major mountain bike trail centre.

The route crosses the main ridge of the Bowland Fells, to the east of its highest ground. Ward's Stone (561m) is the highest ground wholly within Lancashire, beating Pendle Hill by 4m. The highest point in the county is actually on the boundary with Yorkshire, at Green Hill (626m), part of the next mass of high ground north of Whernside.

SLAIDBURN

Slaidburn is one of Lancashire's best-known villages, a tight huddle of stone houses. Even if you're eager to press on, it's worth a quick look around. St Andrew's Church has a three-decker pulpit, box pews and a sanctuary pole. This could be used to bar the church door, allowing a fugitive to secure their claim for sanctuary. Next door, the original grammar school building (1717) survives as part of the junior school. The Hark to Bounty is still an attractive pub, but there's more to it than meets the eye: it contains a courtroom which was first used by travelling justices in the 14th century. At that time it was the only courtroom between Lancaster and York. It was last used in 1937.

STAGE 3
Slaidburn to Whalley

Start	Slaidburn war memorial SD 712 524
Distance	28.1km/17.5 miles
Total ascent	218m/715ft
Steepest climb	13% (just after start)
Ride	Easier than it looks at the start, the initial stiff climb out of Slaidburn being the only major obstacle. The following few kilometres, skirting round Easington Fell, are on quiet upland roads. After Holden you're mostly on rolling roads, with a few abrupt little climbs still lurking about.
OS maps	Entirely covered by Landranger 103 Blackburn and Burnley
Connections	Clitheroe and Whalley have regular direct services to Blackburn, Bolton and Manchester. Change at Blackburn for Preston and the West Coast Main Line. If heading south it might appear easier to go via Manchester, but you'll have to transfer from Victoria station to Piccadilly (about 2km across the city centre).
Accommodation	Little between Slaidburn and the Ribble Valley, then more choice in a string of villages. Camping and Caravanning Club site at Edisford Bridge on the outskirts of Clitheroe. Tents are also welcomed at Three Rivers Park, West Bradford.
Intermediate distances	Holden 8.3km/5.2 miles; Waddington 17.3km/10.9 miles

After Cross O'Greet you may feel like a rest. This isn't it – but it is a much easier stage. There's only one real climb, straight out of Slaidburn, followed by a delightful stretch of upland riding. The roads are quiet and the views extensive: if only there was more like this. But what follows is the Ribble Valley, and that's a reasonable exchange. Maybe it's not so bad to be down among trees and lush pastures again. The Ribble Valley is a classic English rural landscape, with lots of hedgerows and small woods dividing the green pastures. And while Slaidburn might be one of Lancashire's finest villages, so is Waddington.

All roads out of Slaidburn involve a climb. The way we take is probably the easiest, although it may not feel like it. Roll down the street to the river and over the bridge. This is followed by a short sharp climb with a vicious hairpin in the middle. Take a wide line around this corner, following traffic permitting, or it'll feel a lot steeper than the stated 13%.

The gradient soon eases and the road emerges onto rolling upland. Take the second turn to the right, almost straight ahead where the main road veers to the left. The lane dips then climbs gradually onto a broad ridge. Fine views develop over the broad green expanses of Ribblesdale. As the lane gradually trends further right, Pendle Hill shoulders into view.

Looking back at Slaidburn after the first sharp climb

59

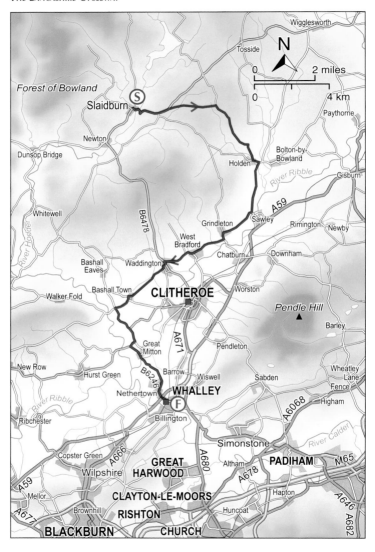

Keep right at a junction. Now there's a long descent with few sharp bends or side-roads to worry about. The surface is mostly decent too, but keep your eyes peeled for the odd rough patch. A steeper section leads to the tiny village of **Holden**. Keep left here and then the road levels out before a T junction by the Copy Nook pub. Turn right for a fairly level ride down the side of the valley. Near Bow Laithe the Ribble joins in from the left. About 1km further on the main road bends left towards **Sawley**. Our route leaves it for a smaller lane on the right, with signs for Grindleton and West Bradford. ▶

The lane skirts close to the river then kicks up in a sharp climb, easing near the school entrance, where you'll be rewarded by elevated views across to Pendle Hill. After another 1km the road reaches **Grindleton**, bends round left and dives back down to the valley.

Swing round right at the bottom and continue into **West Bradford**. Follow the road through the village, with signs for Waddington. After another couple of kilometres the lane reaches a T junction at the upper end of **Waddington** village.

The route goes left then very shortly right, before the church, wriggles round the back of the church and heads

The River Ribble and Pendle Hill from near Sawley

This lane is usually quiet but, as it passes Bowland High, it can get busy at 'school-run' times.

out of the village, bearing right on Twitter Lane (describe it in 140 characters or fewer). Passing Backridge Farm (café/restaurant) it rises gently onto a well-defined ridge between Bashall Brook to the north and the Ribble to the south.

There are good **views across to Clitheroe**, its castle standing out above the town, with Pendle Hill behind. To the north rises Waddington Fell and ahead is the steep, dark end of Longridge Fell.

Continue, and as the ridge begins to dwindle, you get a glimpse of the beautiful Bashall Hall down to the right. ◄ It makes a great picture with its surroundings of green fields, hedgerows, scattered woods, and the brown moors beyond. Just beyond, two houses and Bashall Barn farm shop/café are the sum total of the grandly-named Bashall Town.

Bashall Hall is not open to the public.

At the next T junction go left then quickly right. In another 1km, at a crossroads, go left, as the route shies away from Longridge Fell and turns south, parallel to the River Hodder, hidden down in the valley.

At the next junction turn right on the B6243, follow it round to the right then turn left on the B6246 to ride through **Great Mitton** and onwards to **Whalley**.

SAWLEY AND GRINDLETON

If you've an antiquarian bent you might want to take a short side-trip across the river into Sawley to take a look at the ruins of the Abbey. It's an evocative site, with Pendle Hill looming in the background. The Abbey was founded in 1146 and dissolved by Henry VIII.

Grindleton has two pubs, one called the Duke of York. This is testimony to the fact that, prior to local government reorganisation in 1974, much of this area was in Yorkshire, including everything north of the Ribble and east of the Hodder. In fact, under the old boundaries, you would have entered Yorkshire at Cross O'Greet, and you wouldn't leave it again until you cross the Ribble at Great Mitton. Had there been a Lancashire Cycleway in those days, it would have followed a very different course, missing out most of Bowland but taking in Liverpool and Manchester, plus a swathe of today's

Sawley Abbey requires a short detour

Cumbria, including the Furness and Cartmel peninsulas, Coniston and Hawkshead.

The view across the valley from the lane between West Bradford and Waddington is increasingly dominated by the towering chimney of the Castle cement works, usually with a plume of smoke. This would be conspicuous almost anywhere but in the otherwise overwhelmingly pastoral surroundings of the Ribble Valley it sticks out like a very large sore thumb.

WADDINGTON

The Cycleway route only takes in the upper end of Waddington village, but to whisk straight through misses much of the distinctiveness of the place. With a choice of pubs and a tearoom there are lots of reasons to linger. The Lower Buck Inn (on the route out of the village) is *Good Pub Guide* recommended.

Until well into the 19th century Waddington was an essentially industrial community: there was a cotton spinning mill higher up the stream, and many of the inhabitants were handloom weavers. Bobbins, chairs and other turned wood products were also produced, and there was a tannery. The stream, which still runs through the village, was probably rather less picturesque – and a lot less clean.

GREAT AND LITTLE MITTON

The village of Great Mitton seems anything but Great; there's a church, a pub, a tearoom, the hall and a handful of cottages. But both the church and the hall are ancient and lovely. The nave of All Hallows Church largely dates from 1270, while the tower was added in the 15th century.

The name of the Three Fishes embodies the coat of arms of Whalley Abbey. It claims to have been the first gastropub in Lancashire, although without a clear definition of the term the claim is essentially meaningless. They do do good grub – as does the recently revamped Aspinall Arms, just across the river in Little Mitton. Its vast riverside beer garden is exceptionally tempting on a fine day.

The river separating Great and Little Mitton is not the Hodder but the Ribble. The confluence of the two rivers is just out of sight downstream.

WHALLEY

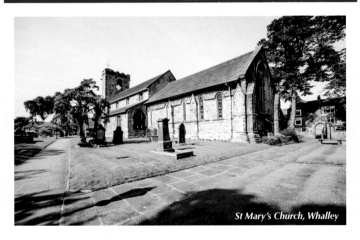

St Mary's Church, Whalley

Tucked away behind the houses and shops in the village centre is St Mary's Church. There are three ancient crosses in the lovely churchyard. Parts of the building date back to the 13th century, but there are known to have been two previous churches in Whalley, which has been a village since Saxon days if not earlier. The pride of the church is its 15th-century choir stalls, originally from Whalley Abbey, but moved here when the monasteries were dissolved by Henry VIII.

Beyond the church is Whalley Abbey, founded in 1296. The first part you come to is the northeast gate, dating from 1480. The west gate, from 1318, straddles the lane further down. The abbey church is now in ruins but the surrounding gardens are lovingly maintained, while the surviving buildings serve the Diocese of Blackburn for conferences and retreats.

Past the west gate you reach another notable structure, the great red-brick railway viaduct of 49 arches, opened in 1850. It is reported that crossing the viaduct struck fear into the hearts of many passengers, so much so that some would get off and walk between Whalley and Billington. A particular feature is the ecclesiastical-looking infill of some of the arches.

THE TOLKIEN CONNECTION

Local tourist brochures and websites make much of the fact that JRR Tolkien wrote parts of *The Lord of the Rings* while staying locally in the 1940s (one of his sons was a teacher at Stonyhurst College). The official Visit Ribble Valley website claims, unblushingly: 'Ribble Valley became his inspiration for Middle-earth'.

Unfortunately this claim is vastly overblown. For a start, *The Hobbit*, precursor to *The Lord of the Rings*, was published in 1937 and conceived even earlier, as was much of the mythology which underlies both stories. It's also well-documented that Tolkien's prime inspiration for the idealised rural idyll of The Shire was the country of his boyhood in rural Warwickshire and Worcestershire.

However, it's quite possible that many details of the setting of *The Lord of the Rings* were suggested by aspects of the area where he spent time during the actual writing of the epic. For instance, the pattern of the three rivers – Ribble, Calder and Hodder – bears some resemblance to his map of The Shire. And, as a lover of good ale, it's highly likely that Tolkien spent a few hours in the Shireburn Arms at Hurst Green, the nearest village to Stonyhurst.

STAGE 4

Whalley to Bilsborrow

Start	Whalley station SD 729 365
Distance	29.2km/18.1 miles
Total ascent	155m/510ft
Steepest climb	Approx 7% (entering Longridge)
Ride	Hardly ever flat, but never very steep either. Billington to Ribchester Bridge is on quiet back lanes. Thereafter roads are a little busier; a minor urban interlude at Longridge.
OS maps	Landranger 103 Blackburn & Burnley; 102 Preston & Blackpool
Connections	After Whalley there are no stations on the route itself, but from Longridge to Bilsborrow the route circles round Preston at a radius of 10–12km.
Accommodation	Nowhere on this stage is very far from a pub or B&B.
Intermediate distances	Ribchester 11.5km/7.1 miles; Longridge 17.5km/10.9 miles

If you follow the 'official' recommendation and start at Whalley, this will be your introduction to the Lancashire Cycleway. As such it will do very nicely; a gentle ride, with gentle scenery, but with the high moors floating on the skyline. Conversely, if you started from Lancaster, you'll be able to look back on those moors with satisfaction, while appreciating the change of pace as the route unwinds into flatter country.

For lovers of history this stage takes some beating, with Whalley Abbey at the start and the Roman remains at Ribchester along the way.

If you've just got off a train you need to turn left along Station Road to a mini-roundabout where a right turn takes you into the centre of the village. If you carry straight on through you may get an impression of some pleasing buildings – marred, usually, by too much traffic

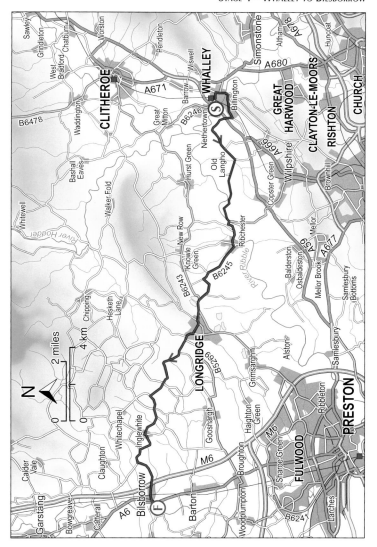

– but you could easily pass Whalley's chief glories (see stage 3) without even suspecting their existence.

Ride down the main street, with the steep front of Whalley Nab rising ahead, to cross the River Calder. The road swings right and rises slightly into the village of **Billington**. Just after St Augustine's RC High School, turn right at a mini-roundabout. The road bridges the busy A59 before swinging left, then left again. Ride through Old Langho (now overshadowed by recent development at Brockhall Village) and pass the Black Bull pub, then take the next right. ◄

This is a pleasant quiet lane, and the last stretch before Salesbury Hall follows the route of a Roman road.

The route drops onto the floodplain of the **River Ribble**, which you cross by the elegant Ribchester Bridge, joining the B6245 to do so. Continue along to **Ribchester**. The direct route goes sharp right, still on the **B6245**, but a detour to the left, into the core of the village, is highly recommended.

> **Salesbury Hall** is a large manor house, almost French in appearance. Don't confuse it with Samlesbury Hall, one of Lancashire's most famous houses, which is about 10km away. Samlesbury Hall isn't on the Cycleway route, although the Southern Loop does pass within about 1km at its closest point.

Continue up the hill towards Longridge, climbing pretty steadily. A final steeper rise brings you into **Longridge** itself. Swing left at the top of this climb then soon turn right into Berry Lane (signposted 'Town Centre') and freewheel down past the shops. ◄

There's a nice little café, Tayah's, by the zebra crossing.

Berry Lane, Longridge

At the end of Berry Lane turn right then, when the road veers right by the Alston pub ('Cyclists welcome'), go straight ahead. It's straight on to Inglewhite now. That is, the road is far from straight but the route is always obvious, there aren't any serious hills, and the surroundings are lushly pastoral. In fact there's very little wrong with this stretch, unless perhaps you suffer from barn-conversion envy.

About 3km out of Longridge is Ye Horns Inn – or is it Horn's? They can't seem to make up their minds about the apostrophe. Another 4km further on is **Inglewhite**, a small village strung around a large green. The Green Man pub here is recommended.

Continue straight ahead through Inglewhite and after a slight climb and short steep descent, keep left (NCN Route 6 goes right here). The road goes over the M6 and the West Coast Main Line then down past Bilsborrow Church to meet the A6 by the Roebuck pub.

With a brace of pubs flanking the junction and an attractive B&B just opposite, **Bilsborrow** seems to have arranged everything very nicely should you want to stop.

RIBCHESTER

The village centre is a clutch of old stone houses and pubs. Apart from the fine 13th-century church the architecture is all modest and domestic, with one exotic touch in the porch of the White Bull: the four pillars which support it are generally believed to be Roman. The rest of the building is 18th century.

The Ribchester Helmet

Ribchester's main claim to fame is as an important Roman site. The remains of the fort of Bremetennacum (some behind the church, some behind the pub) are intriguing rather than spectacular, but certainly worth the short walk. The little museum at the bottom of the street is very nicely set out and has some fascinating relics, most famously the remarkable bronze Ribchester Helmet with its complete hinged face-mask. Also known as the Parade Helmet, this is a ceremonial rather than a fighting helmet. Normally a (very convincing) replica is on show and the original is displayed at the British Museum in London, but in 2014 it was returned on loan to mark Ribchester Museum's centenary. Its value is such that major upgrades to the museum's security system were required.

LONGRIDGE

Longridge is essentially a creation of the Industrial Revolution. The railway to Preston was opened in 1840, primarily to transport stone from local quarries. Several of Preston's principal buildings are built of Longridge Fell gritstone. Following the opening of the railway several cotton mills developed: quarries, mills and railway have all passed into history now.

STAGE 5
Bilsborrow to Great Eccleston

Start	A6/Bilsborrow Lane junction SD 510 396
Distance	44.5km/27.7 miles
Total ascent	122m/400ft
Ride	Another gentle stage, but rarely completely flat. It's mostly quiet until you approach Kirkham, where there's a short urban section. From there to Singleton, the roads tend to be busier; avoid peak periods if you can.
OS maps	Entirely covered by 102 Preston & Blackpool
Connections	Stations at Kirkham and at Poulton-le-Fylde, about 4km from Staining or Singleton on the Blackpool North–Preston line
Accommodation	A scattering of pubs and B&Bs throughout: wider choice in Kirkham
Intermediate distances	Kirkham 16.8km/10.4 miles; Wrea Green 24km/14.9 miles; Singleton 37.7km/23.4 miles

This is not – quite – a flat stage. There are no real climbs, but the route offers just enough undulations to maintain interest. Apart from a brief visit to Kirkham, the atmosphere is essentially one of gently rolling countryside and comfortable villages. Buildings are of brick rather than stone, and there are even a few thatched houses. The backdrop is green fields and woods. It's all a far cry from the image of dark satanic mills.

At Staining you're less than 5km from the sea and from the hilltop you would be able to see it, but it's obscured by the urban ribbon of Blackpool and its satellite towns. Rail and motorway whisk visitors straight to the resort and few of them bother with the hinterland; even when you're almost in the shadow of Blackpool Tower it's pretty quiet. After crossing the A585 the setting becomes even more pastoral and there's just a slight climb to round off the stage.

From the junction by the Roebuck go south down the A6, then turn right into St Michael's Road. This rises slightly over the canal. Continue past the entrance to 'Guy's

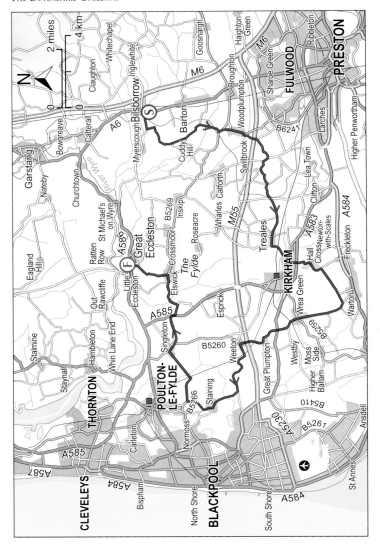

Thatched Hamlet' then take the first left (no signs apart from Cycleway ones) and follow the quiet road through several right-angled bends.

Keep straight on at the first junction, bear left at the next, then go right, on a bend, on Hollowforth Lane. This crosses the canal again by a small marina. At a T junction go left on the B5269 for about 400m, then keep right on the B5411 into **Woodplumpton**.

Beyond the pub and the church swoop down to Woodplumpton Brook. Just after the bridge, where the B5411 swings left, go straight ahead into Sandy Lane. Cross over the M55, then turn right on Bartle Lane. At a T junction turn right on Lea Lane, and after 200m turn left on Blackleach Lane. Keep left at the next fork.

West of Bilsborrow, the route traverses some pretty flat territory

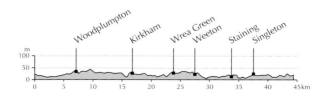

73

*Approaching Kirkham
(rider is travelling
in the opposite
direction to the route
description here)*

Going right instead at the fork – the continuation of Blackleach Lane – will take you in just over 1km to **Roots Café**, a favourite among local cyclists. Keep right at the next junction then turn left just after crossing the M55.

Now it's a fairly straight run for a while, crossing the Lancaster Canal again beside the Hand and Dagger pub (friendly and good value). **Treales** (locally pronounced 'Trails') is a pretty little village with a partly-thatched pub, the Derby Arms. Keep straight on through the village then follow the road round left, down to cross the railway line then up into the outskirts of **Kirkham**. Turn right onto the main road, climb a little more, then drop down into the town centre.

In the bottom of the dip turn left for Freckleton. Cross the **A583** at the lights and follow the road through several bends, past industrial estates and an open prison. There's another big left-hander after the prison. 300 metres further on turn right into Hillock Lane.

Hillock Lane by-passes the substantial villages of Freckleton and Warton, once centres of fishing and boat building. Beyond them lies Warton Aerodrome, constructed during the Second World War and used mainly by American forces. It is now a major manufacturing and testing centre for British Aerospace.

The route continues straight ahead through **Wrea Green**, with the Grapes pub (same chain as the Roebuck in Bilsborrow) on the right and the friendly Dizzy Ducks tearoom on the left. This is Station Road, though there's no station. ▶

There are public toilets alongside the pub car park.

Keep straight on and cross the A583 again at a set of lights. The road swings left and right in **Great Plumpton** and crosses the railway (Preston–Blackpool North line). Having passed the little red-brick church of St Michael's, Weeton, dip under the M55. At the top of the next rise, in **Weeton** village, go left at the T junction (the attractive Eagle and Child pub is 100m to the right).

The road narrows, and the surface deteriorates, at the bridge over the railway; care is required. After this the way twists and turns through open, rolling fields. As the road finally seems to be settling down to a straighter course, turn off right into Chain Lane and continue into **Staining**. ▶

Here there's a connection with NCN Route 62 into Blackpool.

To stick with the Cycleway, turn right on Mill Lane, just after the Plough Inn. Turn right into Smithy Lane, almost opposite the windmill. This swoops down then narrows as it rises again.

At the end there's another T junction. Turn right onto the **B5266** towards Singleton. After a couple of kilometres the route ducks under the railway line. It's a straight run now into **Singleton**, and with any luck the wind will be behind you. Turn right at the junction: the road is called The Village.

Stay with the main road until past the Miller Arms pub, then go left into Mile Road (B5269), signed for Kirkham and Preston. Soon the route crosses the busy **A585**. It's not straight across but right then almost immediately left, still on the B5269. ▶

There are plans to remodel this junction and make it more cycle-friendly.

There's a sharp left on the outskirts of Thistleton. At **Elswick**, just after the Boot and Shoe pub, leave the B5269, turning left for Great Eccleston. There's a slight climb through Copp before reaching **Great Eccleston** itself. A T junction leads into the main street. Turn left to continue to the next stage. To the right are shops, pubs and the excellent Courtyard Caffé. The Farmers Arms in the village is *Good Pub Guide* recommended.

WOODPLUMPTON

Woodplumpton is a long, straggling, unfussy village. At the far end of the village St Anne's Church has neither tower nor spire, just a small belfry. The present church can be traced back to at least the 14th century, but has been rebuilt several times. The lychgate, too, is relatively recent, dating from 1912. The stocks are considerably older. A large boulder in the churchyard is said to mark a witch's grave – she is supposed to have dug herself out when first buried, hence the need for the stone!

KIRKHAM

Kirkham probably had a Roman settlement, linked by road to Ribchester. In 1296 it was granted a charter, allowing markets to be held, and the Market Place – still cobbled – has been in the same location ever since.

WREA GREEN

The village was originally called Wray, but the name was amended to reduce confusion with the other Wray in the Lune valley. The same strategy has not been adopted for the two Wartons: the one we've just by-passed and the one near Carnforth.

It seems fair that the name acknowledges the village green, the largest in Lancashire. The view from the duckpond towards the church is an old faithful for guidebooks and postcards. The village has won many awards in Best Kept Village competitions and the like. Did you know there was an award for Best Kept War Memorial?

SINGLETON

Singleton, with the old fire station on the right

Singleton's history dates back to the Domesday Book, but the entire village was rebuilt in the 1850s and 60s on the orders of Thomas Miller, a Preston industrialist. One hopes the inhabitants were grateful.

Singleton's most striking building is also probably its smallest, a half-timbered structure by the junction of Church Lane. This was built in 1882 as the village fire station but now, prosaically, is an electricity substation. However, the ornamental plasterwork on the side walls is well-maintained and worth a closer look. The first fire engine was horse-drawn and the speed of response to an alarm is said to have depended on how quickly the crew could catch the horse!

STAGE 6
Great Eccleston to Halton

Start	High Street, Great Eccleston SD 426 403
Distance	37.9km/23.5 miles
Total ascent	149m/490ft
Steepest climb	Approx 5%
Ride	Pan-flat for the first half, then a steady but gentle climb after the M6. Postern Gates to Caton is occasionally unpleasant at rush-hour: after Caton a well-surfaced cycle track.
OS maps	Landranger 102 Preston & Blackpool; 97 Kendal & Morecambe
Connections	Nothing on the route itself; later sections are close to Lancaster
Accommodation	No shortage of pubs and B&Bs, especially in and around the villages of Caton and Halton
Intermediate sistances	Stake Pool 8.8km/5.5 miles; Quernmore 27.5km/17.1 miles; Caton 34.7km/21.6 miles

Apart from the swift descent to Cartford Bridge, where a small toll is payable, the first half of this stage is about as flat as it gets. North of the Wyre the undulations have been ironed out completely. The rich black soils of the reclaimed mosslands stretch out under an endless sky. Hills hover on the horizon like a distant memory (or maybe a threat). At times, where the road stands proud above the subsided soil, you'll feel like the highest thing for miles.

It's wind direction, not gradient, which makes the going easy or hard. The prevailing south-westerly will help you all the way, and the main road from Stake Pool to Cockerham is an exhilarating blast when there's a good south-westerly breeze. Of course if you're unlucky and there's a stiff northerly (or worse still, a north-easterly), it can be a real grind.

At Cockerham there's a distinct change of character. Hills make a reappearance; the route makes a feint towards the high Bowland Fells before slipping left along their skirts. There are good views here, reaching to the Lakeland Fells, before the route dips down again into the Lune Valley and the renowned beauty spot of Crook O'Lune.

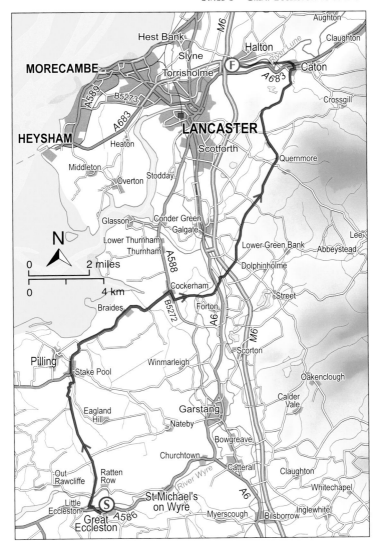

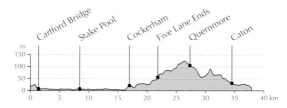

The crossing of the fast A586, which by-passes Great Eccleston, isn't always straightforward. The obvious strategy is to go left then right into Little Eccleston, but you might find it easier to go straight across onto the cycle track and then left along this. Peace and quiet are quickly regained in **Little Eccleston**. Turn right on Cartford Lane, which twists and dives down to Cartford Bridge. The Cartford Inn is *Good Pub Guide* recommended.

You pay the toll after the bridge: it's 20p for bikes and, as far as I know, tandems pay the same, which sounds like a bargain. Immediately after the toll-house turn right, then take the first left, Lancaster Road. The road is virtually dead straight for several kilometres, then gets bored and makes a series of wiggles. Scronkey is the place name but sounds almost like a description. After this assertion of individuality, the road meets the A588 at a T junction in **Stake Pool**. Turn right and follow the A588 to **Cockerham**. ◄

A detour through Pilling village is tempting, and the café at Pilling Pottery is welcoming and good value.

The abrupt rise as you enter Cockerham can be a shock to the system after all that flat stuff. As the road levels out again there's what could be called either a very short dual carriageway or a large traffic island. Turn right here on the **B5272**, then take the first left turn, near the last of the houses.

Swoop down and climb up again, crossing the Lancaster Canal. Continue along the lane, ignoring side turnings, to reach the A6. Go straight across, when traffic permits.

The lane swings left, wrapped tightly around the Bay Horse Inn. It's always hard to pass a cosy-looking pub, harder still when you seem to be almost inside anyway: if you fail to resist you'll find cosy surroundings and fairly up-market food.

Take the turning on the right, under the railway, then climbing steeply round. Take the next left, with signs for Quernmore and Caton, and keep on climbing to a bridge over the M6.

There's a chance for a breather as you drop off the motorway bridge but the road soon rears up again before the next junction, known – for obvious reasons – as Five Lane Ends. Cross, then take the road which climbs half-left. After the initial slope the gradient eases, but the route continues to climb gradually, with only brief respites, for another 3km. Then there's a long swooping descent, interrupted only by the crossroads in **Quernmore** village.

Church and school sit in the valley-bottom, and then there's a short rise to the junction known as Postern Gates. Turn right here. A short descent sets you up nicely for the mostly-level run of about 3km into **Caton**.

Turn right on Copy Lane, by a row of cottages with the intriguing name of Rock'm'Jock. At a T junction go left and down to a mini-roundabout on the **A683**. ▶

The route goes straight across, down the lane left of the Post Office, to meet a cycle path. Turn left on this,

Just along here to the left is the dependable Ship Inn, alongside which is a gnarled oak tree reputed to be 600 years old. Sadly, its last live branch was broken off by a lorry in June 2016 and it's doubtful whether the tree will survive.

St Peter's Church, Quernmore, with Clougha Pike behind

Taking a break at Crook o'Lune, with Ingleborough on the horizon

and it soon reveals itself to be a former railway track. This becomes unmistakable as you cross the **River Lune** at Crook O'Lune.

Even if neither the public toilets nor the refreshment kiosk (good bacon butties) are of interest, it's worth a brief stop at **Crook O'Lune** for the set-piece view up the Lune valley: follow a zig-zag ramp just after the first bridge. The most classical of painters could hardly have composed it better, with the distinctive outline of Ingleborough just where it should be.

Continue on the former railway, crossing the Lune a second time. There are fine views in both directions,

The second bridge at Crook o'Lune

especially south where the peak of Clougha Pike rises above the trees. No further directions are needed for a couple of kilometres until you reach a small car-park by the old station building at **Halton**.

Just beyond this you meet a narrow road. The continuation of the cycle track, straight ahead, leads into Lancaster, so if you started here, finish the job by reversing The Lancaster Link. Turn right and cross the bridge if you started somewhere else, or if it's just been so good you want to go round again.

THE MOSSES

From Cartford Bridge onward, the route crosses a succession of reclaimed mosses: Rawcliffe, Pilling and then Cockerham.

'Moss' in Lancashire means roughly what 'fen' means in East Anglia, and there are many similarities. The peaty soils have shrunk as they have dried out and been worked, and many of the roads are raised above the surrounding fields. Some of the older houses have needed extra steps up to their front doors too.

The Fens may have the same black soils and huge skies, but what the Fens can't offer is the prospect and promise of distant hills. On the long straights of Rawcliffe Moss, assuming it's clear, the road points directly to Scafell and Coniston Old Man. Much nearer, away to the east, are the high moors of the Forest of Bowland.

PILLING

Pilling claims to be England's largest village; this refers not to its population but to the extent of the parish.

As you come into Stake Pool, you cross the line of the former Pilling Railway. The line linking Pilling to the main line at Garstang opened in 1870, and was extended to the coast at Knott End in 1908. The first engine was known as 'The Pilling Pig', apparently because its whistle sounded like a pig having its throat cut, and the name was subsequently applied to the line more generally. A restored engine of this type sits outside Fold House Caravan Park in Stake Pool, about 300m to the left along the A588 from the T junction.

The line was closed in 1965 and few traces now remain apart from a few bridges and former level crossing keepers' cottages.

THE QUERNMORE VALLEY

There's a long steady climb after Five Lane Ends, but there is recompense in the expanding prospect to north and west. Lancaster University is prominent; its original white-topped buildings were intended to create the impression of an Italian hilltown, but later additions haven't maintained this aesthetic. In any case,

Clougha Pike looms over the Quernmore valley

the setting is unmistakably England.

The route runs along the eastern side of the Quernmore valley. Locally pronounced 'Kwormer', the name is derived from 'quern', pronounced as spelt, meaning a millstone. The dark rock which can be seen in several small quarries and on the rocky ridge of Clougha Pike ahead, is Millstone Grit, and millstones were produced here as far back as Roman times.

That ridge has two distinct nicks in its outline: Windy Clough and its smaller neighbour higher up – yes, Little Windy Clough – are the most obvious of several channels scored into the flanks of Clougha Pike. It is believed that they were formed in the final stages of the last Ice Age, when retreating ice was dammed up for a time behind the ridge. Torrents of meltwater, possibly under the ice and under pressure, carved the steep-sided channels through the rock.

At the crossroads in Quernmore, the building on the corner was formerly a pub but ceased to be licensed around 1900. From then until the 1980s it was known as the Temperance Hotel, and the junction is still sometimes referred to as the 'Temp' crossroads. The village has a strong Methodist tradition and the Anglican church stands well to the north, as if it has been banished. Another strong local tradition is the training of sheepdogs. The annual village Field Day, or 'Quernmore Sports', features sheepdog trials, Cumberland and Westmorland Wrestling, and a fell race up Clougha Pike and back.

THE SOUTHERN LOOP
217km/135 miles

The climb above Belmont (Stage 9)

INTRODUCTION

The $64,000 question: is the Southern Loop as good as the Northern?

If you apply thumbscrews and demand a yes/no answer, then it has to be no. But that needs qualifying instantly. A better summary is that most people will find it slightly less good overall. Much will depend on your own particular tastes and interests. If what you're after is pure carefree cycling, the Southern Loop undoubtedly has more urban interruptions than the Northern, but these still amount to less than 10% of the total distance. However, if it's interest you're after, especially human and historical interest, then the Southern Loop is just as rewarding as the Northern, maybe even more so.

And the Southern Loop is different, not merely a pale imitation of the Northern. It is like the Northern Loop in at least one respect: there is plenty of variety. Just when you think you've got a handle on your surroundings, you crest a small climb or round a bend and the scene changes. Sometimes these changes are dramatic – nowhere more so than the first westward view from the summit of the Winter Hill road – while at other times they are more subtle. In any case there is more than enough variety to stop you ever getting bored.

If you start, as described, from Whalley, then you begin your ride on the northern flanks of Pendle Hill, its looming bulk always at your shoulder. Peaceful villages like Pendleton and Worston punctuate the lanes. Downham, a tourist honeypot, is generally less peaceful but no less beautiful. Then you slip round the end of Pendle, out of the Ribble Valley and into lands that were once Yorkshire. It would be easy to whisk through Barnoldswick in a few minutes, and never realise what an interesting small town it actually is.

Earby heralds the climb of Bleara Moor, the toughest on the Southern Loop. If your bottom gear isn't low enough you may vote it the toughest on the entire Cycleway. But, as ever, there is a reward for the effort, with great views back to Pendle, south to the West Pennine moors, and later east into Yorkshire. The Pennine Way passes within a couple of kilometres and you really feel you are on the edge of Lancashire.

After an exhilarating descent to Laneshaw Bridge you begin to climb onto those West Pennine moors. Haworth and 'Brontë Country' are not far away and these moors do have a different feel from those of Bowland. This grows stronger as you climb Deerplay Moor and drop into the Rossendale Valley. The valleys are more urban and the moors above them have a more used look, although in many places they are emptier and quieter now than they have been for centuries. Abandoned farms and dis-used quarries are strewn across the landscape, evocative reminders of a more productive past. Many of the quarries are now frequented by rock climbers and Lee and Cragg quarries, above Bacup, are densely laced with mountain bike trails.

The moors are still economically important as water catchments. There is only one large reservoir in Bowland, but there are strings of them in many West Pennine valleys. Today many are much-loved havens, especially for walking and wildlife-watching. Names like Walves, Wayoh, Entwistle and Delph mark off the kilometres as you approach the high moorland section.

The descent from Winter Hill is thrilling, but take a moment

somewhere to look out to the west. There is a busy urban corridor to cross – although you'll miss all the big towns – before the flatlands beckon. Though there's a surprise in store before you get there, as the soft green hills around Parbold turn out to be bigger than they looked.

As you spiral off Ashurst's Beacon, the transition is complete. A few more, barely perceptible undulations, then a stretch of utter flatness, a region that once was all swamp and lake. At Martin Mere there are glimpses of that past. Elsewhere the land, drained and intensively worked, spreads black soils under vast skies. On some smaller lanes, the drops into the drainage ditches are occasionally alarming.

Gradually you work round back towards the hills. After Croston, something of a showpiece, the third

Pendle Hill from just above York (Croston to Whalley – Stage 11)

dimension begins to reassert itself. You skirt Leyland and re-cross the urban band threaded by motorways and railways. This is another of those short, inescapable sections that you have to do in order to enjoy the rest of it.

At Johnson's Hillock you can start to enjoy yourself again. In fact the following section is, for me, one of the most memorable of the whole Cycleway. This is probably the best piece of route-finding on either loop. It feels as if you are uncovering a well-kept secret. In the very centre of Lancashire, right between Preston and Blackburn, there is a little piece of deep countryside, as winsome as it is surprising.

As you cross the main Preston – Blackburn road there's yet another change of scene. A solid climb through Mellor leads to a ride along the crest of a ridge. It's poised between Blackburn on one hand and, on the other, the Ribble Valley, Pendle Hill and the Forest of Bowland. The contrast seems to encapsulate Lancashire.

One last set of traffic lights, one last small climb, a freewheel down to the outskirts of Whalley, and the fat lady is loosening her vocal chords.

It may not be the grandest, or most beautiful, section of the whole, but if I had to suggest one short ride that would give a stranger a real idea of the warp and weft of Lancashire, I would suggest that trip from Whittle-le-Woods to Whalley. It seems only fitting that this road lies at the very heart of the county. So, if you want a reason to start at Whalley, maybe you'll find it in finishing at Whalley.

Having said that, there is no one obvious starting point for the Southern Loop, in the way that Lancaster is pre-eminent for the Northern. As the Connections notes make clear, there are many other railway stations scattered around the loop. However, for those arriving from other parts of the country, a stop on the West Coast Main Line is far and away the most convenient. Hence The Wigan Link, connecting Wigan North Western station with the Cycleway: see Stage 9a.

STAGE 7
Whalley to Laneshaw Bridge

Start	Whalley station SD 729 365
Distance	37.3km/23.2 miles
Total ascent	648m/2125ft
Steepest climb	Approx 18% (Bleara Moor)
Ride	Quiet lanes after Whalley, with a stretch of cycle track alongside the busy A59. After Downham there's a section of very minor lane, with several gates. Broader roads through Barnoldswick; Earby heralds the big climb and descent to Laneshaw Bridge.
OS maps	Landranger 103 Blackburn & Burnley
Connections	Whalley has regular trains to Blackburn, Bolton and Manchester. Laneshaw Bridge is about 4km/2.5 miles from Colne, which has services to Blackburn and Preston.
Accommodation	The Ribble Valley is well provided with places to stay. YHA hostel at Earby; book well ahead, as it's close to the Pennine Way. Luxury accommodation at the Alma Inn, above Laneshaw Bridge.
Intermediate distances	Downham 12.5km/7.8 miles; Barnoldswick 24.5km/15.2 miles

Do you prefer to put things off, or to get them over with? It's worth asking because this stage, which many will do as the start of the Southern Loop, includes the toughest climb on the entire loop, Bleara Moor. Cross O'Greet, on the Northern Loop, is considerably longer, but not as fierce.

The route starts gently enough, skirting round the massive bulk of Pendle Hill (the feared climb of Nick O'Pendle is not on our route.) Apart from the need to cross the A59 a couple of times it's all very quiet and bucolic, like the slow movement from a pastoral symphony. However, there's a change of key at the small town of Barnoldswick, and the crescendo soon follows as you climb onto Bleara Moor. Reaching the top is worth a fanfare, especially on a clear day. There are great views north and west from the top of the climb and then, as the road loops round the hills before the descent, to the east also. And that descent is one of the best too.

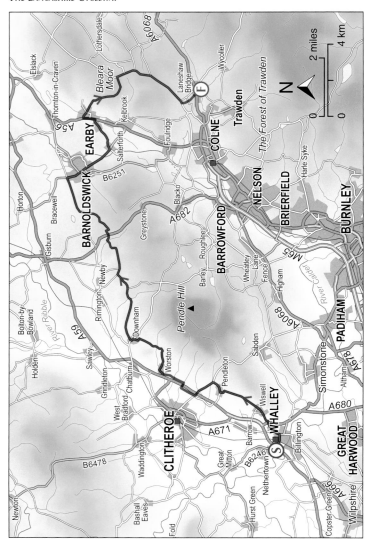

90

From Whalley station turn left, towards the village centre. At the mini-roundabout turn left (unless you want to explore the village first). After 400m fork right by a prominent half-timbered house onto Wiswell Lane. Climb steadily, cross the A681 and keep on climbing. As you reach **Wiswell** keep right (signed for Pendleton). The lane, still climbing, follows the edge of the village, which has many fine old stone houses clustered around narrow streets and alleys.

Eventually the lane levels off near Cold Coats, having climbed about 100m since Whalley. You can freewheel down into **Pendleton** (watch out for tight bends

The old school, Pendleton

just before the village). Turn right, climb slightly past the church and the old school then contour along to a T junction.

Turn left and whizz down to the busy A59, where there's a staggered crossing for cyclists. Follow the road on the other side for about 100m then turn right on a narrow lane, marked as a dead end except for cycles. Follow this, almost parallel to the A59, then re-cross the main road. ◄ It looks as if you're heading across into a rough field-entrance, but in fact the cycle track on the other side proves to have a reasonable surface. This shadows the main road for another 1km or so before joining a secluded lane. Go right at its end into **Worston**.

This can take some time!

> **Worston** is not one of the valley's showplaces, and none the worse for that, but it does have the Calf's Head, which proclaims itself to be a 'country restaurant, hotel & watering hole'.

Beyond the lane quickly narrows to single-track width, with passing places. The local tourist map subtly discourages motorists from using this road, and it's delightfully quiet. Although Pendle Hill looms massively ahead, the route doesn't climb too much, and slips without any real fuss between Pendle's bulk and the smaller, conical, Worsaw Hill. Beyond this, the road eases gently down into **Downham**.

> Observant travellers will notice **outcrops of limestone** on the flanks of Worsaw, which is a reef knoll, or more specifically a Waulsortian mudmound, where muddy deposits accumulated around a coral reef in the warm shallow seas of the Carboniferous period. Its species-rich grassland also makes it a Biological Heritage Site.

Turn left. Climb the hill towards the church, but fork right just before the steepest bit. After leaving the village the road runs broadly level at first, but several streams cut across the slope, making for sharp dips in and climbs out again. Keep straight ahead at successive junctions and presently (about 5km from Downham) the lane dwindles still further, appearing little more than a gated track, although it is still a public highway. Having to dismount to open the gates – and close them again, of course – may be mildly irksome, although on my last visit I found all but the first propped open anyway. There's little traffic along here. ▸

Climb up to the last gate and just beyond is the A682. Go straight across into Stocks Lane (still quiet, but no more gates) which weaves downhill, with fine views across the valley of Stock Beck and the lower reaches of Ribblesdale, backed by the hills of the Yorkshire Dales. After Brogden Hall, with some fine stone buildings, the weaving stops. This straighter section follows the line of a Roman road, which ran from from Ribchester to Tadcaster in Yorkshire.

At a T junction go right on the B6251 and down into **Barnoldswick**. Keep virtually straight ahead through the town, following the B6383. As you leave town it becomes wide, straight and not too trafficky, but there's a cycle lane if you prefer it. The road sweeps down, over the Leeds and Liverpool Canal, then levels out into **Salterforth**. Go left then keep right on Earby Road.

We once had a memorably close encounter with a Little Owl perched sleepily in a hawthorn near Middop Hall.

Evening light, near Brogden Hall

At **Earby**, turn left along the A56 then fork right by the Co-operative food store into Victoria Road, signed for Lothersdale. Follow the road, which curves right to a small roundabout. Take the third exit, Water Street. At a fork, keep right on Stoney Bank Lane (the left fork leads to the youth hostel). Ignore side turnings and climb steadily, then more steeply.

This first pitch isn't too bad, but it ramps up as the road bends right. There's an uncomfortably narrow section, which is followed by the steepest bit of all.

It smacks of cruel and unusual punishment to throw a **near-20% gradient** at you after you've already done a fair chunk of 12–15%. However, the good news is a) it's quite short, b) that's most of the climbing done and c) there's a picnic area at the top. A café would be nice, but at least there are tables to sit at and a sweeping view to admire once the red mist has cleared.

There is another lesser rise before the road swings round and contours the flanks of Bleara Moor. At the next T junction go right and dive down, past the turning to Lothersdale. Just watch any drivers who may be about to turn into or out of that side road, as they won't always realise that you could be clocking 50–60kph here. If no-one interferes you get a grand head start for the rise on the other side. It's a steady enough climb anyway. Heroes of Bleara Moor will laugh at it. And just over the top there's a pub.

Whether or not you take on extra ballast, the next 2km are a glorious, almost straight, downhill run. But don't get too carried away and miss the left turn at the bottom, into Long Lane (signed for Wycoller Country Park). The Alma Inn's promise of 'good food and real ale' may lose some of its allure at the top of Long Lane, when you see that it's off route and uphill, whereas the route goes left into Emmott Lane for a freewheel down to **Laneshaw Bridge**. At the bottom go left onto the A6068 and instantly right into School Lane.

PENDLETON

Pendleton is a striking village with a 'dual-carriageway' main street divided by an attractive stream, and in a less-favoured part of the world would be a major attraction in its own right. But the Ribble Valley is almost awash with pretty villages – Worston and Downham just ahead, Waddington on the Northern Loop, Bolton-by-Bowland and several more. Pendleton does attract visitors, but it isn't a major tourist honey-pot. You may feel that it is all the better for it, and no doubt many of its inhabitants would agree with you.

The Swan with Two Necks (150m to the left when you reach the main village street) is unpretentious and welcoming; it was CAMRA's National Pub of the Year in 2013. The most likely explanation for the curious name is that it is a corruption of 'Swan with Two Nicks'. A nick (cut) in the bill is a traditional method of marking swans – unlike most wild birds, swans are generally considered to belong to someone, usually the Crown.

DOWNHAM

Unlike Pendleton or Worston, Downham definitely is one of the valley's showpieces. 'Picturesque' is probably the word for the lines of dark stone cottages running up the hill to the church, or nowadays we might say 'telegenic'. For a long time Downham's greatest claim to fame was that it was the location for the film *Whistle Down the Wind*. This was shot way back in 1961, and you probably can't get it on Netflix, but they have long memories in the Ribble Valley. However *Whistle Down the Wind* gets second billing now, as Downham was the principal location for the filming of BBC TV's family drama *Born and Bred* between 2001 and 2005.

Downham is particularly suitable as a film and television location because of the absence of overhead cables and television aerials in the village. This is enforced by the Assheton family, who still live in Downham. Unfortunately, the location of the main car park means that most visitors' cars go through the village twice, once on arrival and once on leaving. This definitely detracts from its picturesqueness at busy periods.

Downham Ice Cream Shop, on your way into the village, also serves snacks and hot drinks. The Assheton Arms, opposite the church at the top of the hill, became the Signalman's Arms in the TV series. It does very good food, if you can squeeze in.

PENDLE HILL AND THE PENDLE WITCHES

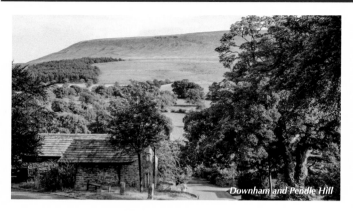

Downham and Pendle Hill

From the area around Downham's church and pub there's a classic view over the rest of the village, with Pendle Hill rising beyond. This is as good a place as any to say a little about the Pendle Witches, although the 'real' witch country is on the other side of the hill and the Cycleway route doesn't visit it. Genuine historical events underlie the various tales that have been spun (the best is still Robert Neill's 1951 classic *Mist over Pendle*). In 1612 seven women and two men from the Pendle area were hanged following a trial at Lancaster Castle. Some had actually confessed to the practise of witchcraft, but of course we know today that under sufficient pressure many people will confess to crimes they have not committed. It is hardly possible now to say whether any of the accused were 'genuine' witches, whatever that might mean.

Pendle Hill is to Lancashire what Ingleborough is to Yorkshire – not the highest hill in the county but the best known and most recognisable, shouldering into view from many points on both loops of the Cycleway. It's worth recording that Pendle Hill means 'Hill Hill Hill'. It is such a dominant presence that it's easy to imagine just calling it 'the Hill' – 'Pen' in early Celtic language. Much later, this meaning was forgotten and it became 'the hill called Pen,' or Pendle. Yet again this meaning was lost and it became 'the hill called Pendle', or Pendle Hill. Furthermore, this name was applied to the wider district, and many people now think the hill is named for the area, when it's really the other way around.

96

BARNOLDSWICK

Like much of Bowland and the Ribble Valley, before local government reorganisation in 1974 Barnoldswick (local pronunciation: 'Barlick') was in Yorkshire, and it seems that many of the inhabitants still feel an allegiance to the White Rose. If you go straight through on the Cycleway route you barely glimpse the picturesque town square, which has a number of specialist shops, cafés and occasionally a town crier.

Barnoldswick was the site of an attempt to found a Cistercian Abbey in the 12th century, as an offshoot of Fountains Abbey. However the monks did not get on with the locals and eventually abandoned their efforts, decamping to a new site at Kirkstall, near Leeds. A few years later, not wishing to appear totally defeated, some of the monks returned to build the church of St Mary-le-Gill, but they built it a good mile from the town centre and it still stands in an isolated position.

The town developed as a weaving centre, first for wool and later for cotton, and in the early 20th century there were 13 mills, with around 22,000 looms. As happened throughout Lancashire, foreign competition and the advent of artificial fibres led to the decline of the industry. The last mills in Barnoldswick closed in the early 1980s; Bancroft Mill remains as a museum, complete with working steam engine. Some of the mills were requisitioned during the Second World War for the manufacture of aero engines. Rolls-Royce still produces aero engine components here.

The tradition of fine engineering is also sustained, with direct relevance to cycling, by Hope Technology. Originally an aerospace subcontractor, they were among the first companies to make disc brakes for mountain bikes, initially as a private project (the owners were keen mountain bikers). They then began to sell the brakes and moved into producing other bike parts. In 2000 the company became purely a maker of bicycle components. Although best known for mountain bike 'bits' they also make parts such as hubs and disc brakes for road and cyclo-cross bikes too. They also sponsor a number of riders in cyclo-cross and various mountain bike disciplines.

STAGE 8
Laneshaw Bridge to Holcombe Brook

Start	A650/School Lane junction, Laneshaw Bridge SD 923 407
Distance	43.9km/27.3 miles
Total ascent	691m/2265ft
Steepest climb	Approx 10% a couple of times
Ride	To Walk Mill is mostly rural; plenty of substantial climbs. Up and down Deerplay Moor is long but gradual; Rossendale Valley has a few undulations. Rawtenstall and Haslingden are busy, but compact: the last stretch to Holcombe is gentler still.
OS maps	Landranger 103 Blackburn & Burnley; 109 Manchester
Connections	Limited: Laneshaw Bridge is about 4km/2.5 miles from Colne, for Blackburn and Preston. Bury is served by Manchester's Metrolink trams, which don't carry bikes. For Bolton see Stage 9.
Accommodation	A scattering of pubs and B&Bs early on; YHA-approved camping barn close to the route just beyond Trawden. Group accommodation at Coldwell Activity Centre; more choice in Rossendale Valley
Intermediate distances	Worsthorne 14.8km/9.2 miles; Water 25.5km/15.8 miles; Haslingden 35.8km/22.2 miles

This is more like Lancashire as 'offcomers' – non-local visitors – tend to visualise it, with plenty of terraced houses and mill chimneys. But you'll often be looking down on them, even on the chimneys. This may be the Lancashire of long industrial heritage, but it's confined to steep-sided valleys and narrow cloughs. Above, always, are the moors. Quarrying may have nibbled at their edges, but for the most part the moors are as wide and open as ever.

They're changeable, these moors. On a good day they are exhilaratingly expansive. On a bad day, especially in a headwind, they can seem almost unbearably bleak. This is when it's good to know that, whatever it may feel like, they don't actually go on for ever. On days like this you'll probably be glad to drop into the shelter of the Rossendale Valley. This is urban without the sprawl, and all the better for it.

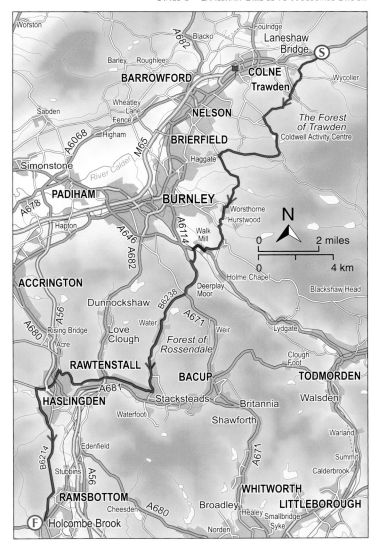

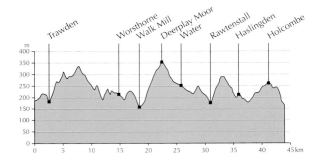

After joining the A6068 at Laneshaw Bridge, turn right into School Lane: there are signs for Wycoller Country Park. After 100m, just over the bridge, go right again into Carriers Row, where there is indeed a fine row of stone cottages. After a steady climb the road levels off on an open shelf below the broad moors. Go left at the next junction, then right. ◄

This is where the Sunday drivers turn off left to Wycoller.

The road now drops into **Trawden**. At the bottom you pass the (very welcoming) Old Rock Café just before a T junction. Turn left. After a climb, fork R below a church, then immediately L on Burnley Rd. There's still a good couple of kilometres climbing ahead, with one brief dip in the middle. It ends at the crossroads by Clarion House, perched prominently on the skyline. Go left here for a rapid descent to Coldwell. ◄

There's a handy tearoom at the activity centre here.

'Nestle' is a grossly overworked word. In tourist blurbs and some guidebooks every second village nestles. But **Trawden**, folded tight in a narrow clough, merits it more than most places. The only problem is that nestling generally implies being surrounded by steep slopes, and Trawden is no exception. Indeed the name probably comes from the Old English *trog denu*, meaning 'trough-shaped valley'.

The road wriggles round the reservoir, climbs a bit more, then swings right past a pillbox. After another minute or two of climb, there's a sudden view ahead, over **Burnley** in its bowl of hills. There's a parking area by the start of the descent, but can those who have merely driven up appreciate the view as much as those of us who've made a real effort to get here?

They certainly can't get as much enjoyment from the swooping descent, straight for a couple of kms, then twisting down through Lane Bottom before it kicks up into **Haggate**.

> From this approach, **Haggate** seems like an isolated village, but it is actually on the edge of the built-up area of Brierfield, which itself fills the gap between Burnley and Nelson.

At the crossroads in Haggate, bracketed by pubs, a left turn launches another swift descent. If you're lucky with the traffic, and confident in your cornering, you can carry plenty of speed across the bridge to set you up for the next climb.

This has one of those ominous arrows on the map. It's the first – in fact the only – one on this stage. However, the steep section comes early and is quite short. The road twists and dips past a pub, then makes another rise before easing off and running down into **Worsthorne** which, although surrounded by a rash of recent housing, retains the old stone core of the village. You go almost straight ahead, to the right of the village store. There's a café on the corner, too, and a brace of pubs nearby.

Drop down gently from the village, then climb to a T junction and turn left. Descend through Mereclough into Over Town. Watch out here for a sharp right turn into Mount Lane, followed by a steep descent to **Walk Mill**, with a tight hairpin at the bottom. Just after this you meet the busy A646. Turn right.

Pass under the railway then turn left on a narrow lane, signed as a cul-de-sac except for bikes. Climb pleasantly to a T junction, turn right, then turn left on the A671 to continue climbing steadily. ▶ The road swings into a small side-valley and keeps rising. If you can ignore the

There's a small layby after about 1 km, but its views up the Cliviger Gorge are now rather obscured by trees.

Looking towards Cliviger Gorge, from the climb on the A671

traffic, the sustained but reasonable gradient makes this a thoroughly enjoyable climb. Just as the road emerges onto the wide open spaces of **Deerplay Moor**, turn right – with care – onto the **B6238**, signed for Rawtenstall.

The road descends gently at first, then a little more steeply, through the ribbon villages of **Water**, Lumb and Whitewell Bottom. The valley sides grow higher. As you reach another cluster of old mills on the left, look for a street on the right called Bridleway. Climb this to a T junction, then turn right on a street called Turnpike.

Keep climbing. Gradually the gradient eases and the surface improves and then it's a steady roll down down, past a lot of handsome stone houses, into **Rawtenstall** town centre, or at least to the fringe of the centre.

At the traffic lights go (almost) straight across into **Haslingden** Old Road and start climbing again. It's steep at first but soon becomes more gradual, and it goes on a long way. You can take a break halfway, if necessary, in the café at the ski-slope, but it's probably best to keep plugging away for another 5 or 10 minutes to the aptly named Height End. ◀

This really is the last serious climb until well into the next section.

The road contours round, with a glimpse of the Halo (see 'Panopticons') ahead and good views over

Haslingden and the moors beyond. The valley opposite, marked by three reservoirs, is Haslingden Grane.

Haslingden Grane offers a striking example of rural depopulation. Once it was home to over 1000 people, mostly quarry workers, farmers, and handloom weavers. The construction of the reservoirs in the mid-19th century flooded the better land, but the community struggled on until the 1880s, when there was a major agricultural crisis, with drastic falls in commodity prices.

Soon there's a swinging, swooping descent. As you come into Haslingden town centre, go almost straight on into Deardengate, over a short section of setts (they're not cobbles: cobbles are round), then left at the traffic lights. Go second right into Warner Street then dog-leg across into Grane Road, which forms the B6232 for Darwen.

Speed down under the dual carriageway and up the other side, with a sharp left turn at the top onto the B6235, signed for Helmshore. The road passes the Textile Museum at Helmshore and continues along the side of the Irwell Valley to Holcombe – a fine elevated section.

Now the road tips down and you can freewheel to the T junction with the A676. Go right and almost at once there are traffic lights. This is **Holcombe Brook**.

WYCOLLER

Although it's a couple of kms off the Cycleway route, Wycoller is worth a mention. Once a busy community of handloom weavers, it could not compete with larger powered mills and became an isolated backwater. Preserved by neglect, the village was 'rediscovered' in the late 20th century. Wisely, visitors are not allowed to bring cars into the village itself and if you go when it's not buzzing with tourists it really can feel as if it has been preserved in aspic.

Wycoller is only about 14km across the hills from Haworth, and the Brontë family certainly knew the area well. It is thought that Wycoller Hall, now in ruins, was already derelict when the Brontës knew it, and it may well have given Charlotte the inspiration for Ferndean Manor in 'Jane Eyre'.

PANOPTICONS

As you turn onto the B6238 at the crest of Deerplay Moor, another road goes immediately right again. This leads after about 1.2km to a car-park from which a 300m walk leads to the Singing Ringing Tree, probably the best known of four 'panopticons' scattered around Pennine

The Halo, above Haslingden

Lancashire. The 3m-high Singing Ringing Tree makes organ-like music when the wind blows. However, it's not just 1.2km there and 1.2km back; there's a steep climb and descent on each leg. Don't say you weren't warned.

The panopticons are sculptural structures placed in prominent positions and commanding panoramic views. The Atom stands on the hillside above Wycoller and Colourfields is in Blackburn.

The only one you'll actually see from the Cycleway is the Halo above Haslingden. This can be visited fairly easily if you wish: as the climb out of Rawtenstall levels off at Height End, look for a byway on the right, Oakenhead Wood Old Road. Turn up this for a short way then go left (behind some houses) along a track. Fork right to arrive at the parking area near the Halo. Descend the lane to its left to return to the main route.

ROSSENDALE

There's no sign of deer on Deerplay Moor today, but once this whole area – still labelled 'Forest of Rossendale' on OS maps – was a royal hunting forest. As in Bowland, the term 'forest' can be deceptive: tree cover was generally sparse or non-existent, then as now. You have to go back much further in time to find general tree-cover over most of the Pennine uplands. Large-scale clearance for cultivation occurred in the Bronze Age, before about 1000BC. The soils became exhausted and this, coupled with a change in climate, led to the formation of peat bogs.

Hunting forest status ended in the late 15th century and the land was parcelled out into vaccaries (cattle farms). On the poor soils the economy was nearly always marginal and handloom weaving was a vital addition to household incomes. The steep valley sides and ample supplies of water offered the right conditions for the development of larger mills in the 18th and 19th centuries, but while the population in the valleys grew, many of the higher farms ceased to be viable.

A later development was the manufacture of felt. It is thought that some workers made themselves slippers from waste scraps of felt and that this was the origin of the footwear industry which also became a major force in the valley. Most of the cotton mills have now closed, but footwear is still a significant local industry: some sites are now merely sales outlets, and much of what they sell is imported.

Rawtenstall has a good indoor market and a pleasant high street, but perhaps its most singular claim to fame is as the home of Britain's last surviving Temperance Bar. 'The Pub with No Beer', as it describes itself, is in Fitzpatrick's Herbal Health Shop at 5 Bank Street. Here you can quench your thirst, as god-fearing mill workers did, on such delights as Blood Tonic, Lemon Punch, Sarsaparilla and the famous Black Beer. It's closed at the time of writing but apparently is due for a revamp and will re-open: no date has yet been given.

THE IRWELL VALLEY

The road passes the textile museum at Helmshore, which comprises two working mills, one still powered by a waterwheel. It recreates the atmosphere of the industry's heyday as well as any museum in the county. Its future has been called into question due to cuts in council funding but there's real hope that new backers will be found.

Around Holcombe there are semi-aerial views of Ramsbottom. If you think you can see a steam train down there, you're probably right. The East Lancashire Railway was opened in 1846, linking Rawtenstall and Ramsbottom with Bury and Manchester. It closed in 1972 but was revived by a group of enthusiasts, with local authority help, and re-opened in 1991. Trains, often steam-hauled, currently run between Rawtenstall and Bury, with some services extending another 6km east to Heywood.

Looking up and right rather than down and left around Holcombe, you can hardly miss the tall outline of the Peel Tower (aka Holcombe Tower or Peel Monument). Opened in 1852 and funded by public subscription, the tower commemorates Sir Robert Peel (1788–1850). Born in Bury, Peel was Home Secretary from 1822–1830 and is best remembered for establishing the Metropolitan Police, which provided a model for modern police forces across the country. He later became Prime Minister (1834–1835 and 1841–1846).

THE RAKE

Just beyond Holcombe church, whose spire is obvious on the left, anyone interested in cycle racing might like to take a short detour along Chapel Lane, which doubles back on the left. Near the church it dips down very sharply. You'd have to be very interested in cycle racing to make this descent and then climb back up.

This is 'The Rake'. This upper section – which maxes out at around 23% – lends its name to the longer climb, right from Ramsbottom town centre. The course is 875m long and has an average gradient of 12%. The record time is an incredible 2mins 14 secs. Simon Warren's book *100 Greatest Cycling Climbs* gives it a rating of 8/10.

Originally, members of the Bury Cycling Club vied to see who could get farthest before falling off. This challenge developed into a time-trial, held annually in October. It is one of the most famous cycling hill-climb races. The Rake also hosted the national championship in 1999, 2005 and 2012.

Most people will be heartily glad that the Lancashire Cycleway does not include any such intense climbs. And many will be much more interested in the admirable Shoulder of Mutton pub, which stands just beyond the junction. This is a friendly place with several cosy small rooms, good beer and good food too. If there's one drawback, it's that it can get a little too popular at weekends.

STAGE 9

Holcombe Brook to Appley Bridge

Start	Traffic lights, Holcombe Brook SD 780 153
Distance	43.6km/27.1 miles
Total ascent	470m/1540ft
Steepest climb	Approx 9% (Turton Bottoms)
Ride	Short, steep and twisting around Edgworth and Chapeltown, then more moderate gradients. Steep descent off Winter Hill; then a more urban section in Adlington. A couple of tedious km on the A49, then quiet roads once more
OS maps	Start on Landranger 109 Manchester, finish on 108 Liverpool
Connections	Near the start of the stage head down into Bolton for connections to Blackburn, Manchester, Preston and points beyond. Entwistle is on the Bolton–Blackburn line, and Adlington on the Bolton–Preston one. Appley Bridge for the Wigan–Southport line (West Coast Main Line at Wigan)
Accommodation	A significant gap mid-stage, apart from the Black Dog Inn, Belmont (recommended). Earlier and later parts are better-supplied with pubs and B&Bs.
Intermediate distances	Belmont 16.6km/10.3 miles; Adlington 25.3km/15.7 miles; Coppull Moor 33.2km/20.6 miles

Sir Bradley Wiggins once said (on BBC Radio 4, so it must be true) that Rivington Pike is his favourite place to ride. Unless he does more mountain biking than we're aware of, he must have been referring to the road, included in this stage, over the moors north of the Pike itself. And as you start the descent you'll surely see why.

The urban surroundings of the previous stage fall quickly behind as the route explores the southern valleys of the West Pennine moors. There are a few villages at first, then some long, lonely stretches. The culminating climb over the shoulder of Winter Hill opens up vast views across the lowlands of west Lancashire, and the descent signals a marked change in scenery. There's another urban corridor to negotiate around Adlington before the

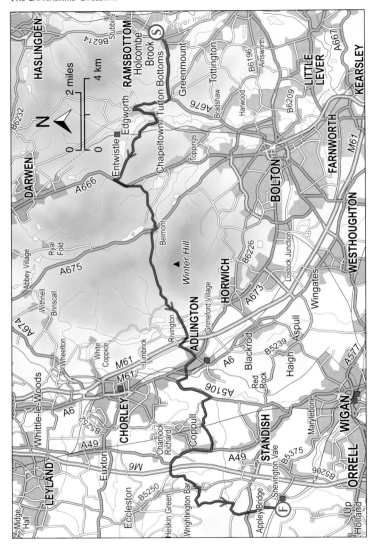

route regains more rural surroundings. Once west of the M6, things become distinctly more tranquil for a while.

From the traffic lights in Holcombe Brook go straight ahead on the A676 in the direction of Bolton. There's a short climb, soon easing to give a fairly level run through Hawkshaw. Pass the small Walves reservoir on the right, and make a short climb. It's easy to overshoot the sneaky right turn at the top, signed for Edgworth and Entwistle. The building on the corner is a former pub, with 'Bull's Head' still over the door.

Sweep down past the end of the reservoir and all too soon start climbing again. It eases gradually before the crossroads in **Edgworth**, where there's a choice of pubs. Go left, weaving down the hill into **Turton Bottoms**, then up again. Turn sharp right after 1 mile, joining the B6391: it looks from the map as if this will be a T junction, but it isn't. Climb a bit more into **Chapeltown** High Street.

The name **Chapeltown** is slightly puzzling, as there's not a chapel in sight, only the handsome St Anne's Church, parish church to the whole Edgworth area. Anyway, it has a fine array of

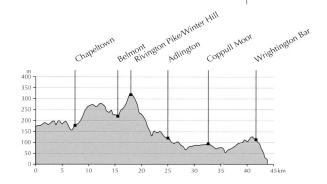

cottages, all very pretty and flowery. The Chetham Arms says 'Walkers Welcome' and so are cyclists.

Shortly after crossing over the railway (Bolton–Blackburn) you pass a turning to the right, Batridge Rd, which provides access to Entwistle station if required.

After Chapeltown the road begins to climb out onto the moors again, but it takes it steadily, with no sudden brutalities lurking round the next bend. ◄

At a T junction turn left onto the **A666**. As the main route between Blackburn, Darwen and Bolton, it's usually busy: 666, the 'Number of the Beast' may seem quite appropriate. There's no alternative but to grin and bear it for about 700m, and then it can be a bit awkward making the right turn. This comes just after the main road swings left, and is signed for the 'Pit Stop' tea wagon, which is found a short way down the side road.

Where the tea wagon traffic goes left to re-join the main road, swing right. The road gets narrower; there's a view ahead to Winter Hill before it dives to a stream. Then there's a level, open stretch before a crossroads. Go straight across, drop down steeply and then more gradually. Pass through a small works complex, some of it now being redeveloped as housing, before a slight rise to the A675. Turn right into **Belmont**. At the Black Dog pub

Lane before Belmont, with Winter Hill looming

Rivington Reservoir, Winter Hill (with mast) and Rivington Pike (with tower) behind

turn left (or stop for refreshment). The rest of the climb is surprisingly mild, so you don't need to worry overmuch about doing it on a full stomach.

After passing a small pool known locally, and flatteringly, as the Blue Lagoon, there's just a short rise or two before the moors open out. The top of the climb naturally offers a grand view, but it opens out even more as you descend. ▶ Sweep past left- and right-branching lanes.

There's a tearoom on the left just before the bottom: if you get to **Rivington** village green you've gone past it. At the green turn right and cross the dam of Rivington reservoir (there's another tearoom overlooking the dam). After this there's a slight rise and then a T junction. The roar of traffic seems threatening, but it comes from the M61, just a field away. At the T junction go right. The road draws closer to the motorway before swinging up round and across it. Go left, alongside the Bay Horse Inn, then swoop down into **Adlington**.

At the traffic lights turn right on the A673 for about 1km. ▶ At the second mini-roundabout turn left into Rawlinson Lane, over the railway line (Manchester–Preston), straight across the A6 then over the Leeds and

This is a truly great descent, but watch out for sheep and potholes, especially in the upper reaches.

For Adlington railway station go straight across at the lights.

111

Liverpool Canal. The road swings right and up, then levels out and meets the **A5106**.

Go left for about 3km, first down then up again. On the crest, opposite the Thyme and Place bar and restaurant, turn right into Jolly Tar Lane. This is quite narrow at first, though fortunately not too busy. Keep left as it swings through open fields and soon there's a bit more elbow room. At a crossroads flanked by new houses, go left and over another railway bridge (West Coast Main Line this time) then along into Coppull Moor. On meeting the **A49**, turn right.

Follow the A49 for 3km, through Coppull Moor and the outskirts of **Charnock Richard** to a roundabout. Go left here, signed 'Eccleston'. Just after crossing over the M6, turn left on a quiet lane which dives swiftly into a wooded valley. Keep left as it forks, halfway up the climb out on the other side, then level out to **Wrightington Bar**.

Go straight(ish) across the B5250, into Church Lane. As the village peters out, you'll just be starting to wonder how you've missed the church, when suddenly it appears, in an isolated but splendid position. The long gradual fall of land to the north produces an expansive view towards Preston and the Ribble Valley, with the Bowland Fells beyond, and the Lake District peaks also visible on a clear day.

Just past the church there's a T junction. Go left, into Toogood Lane. That may be a slight exaggeration, but very pleasant it certainly is. After a couple of kms go right at another T junction and follow the road round to the left and on to meet the A5209. OS maps identify this junction as 'Dangerous Corner', which is alarming, but the crossing of the A-road is merely awkward, with a slight dog-leg.

> The name arises from **a local legend** about a woman who was being carried to her funeral. Rounding the corner, the coffin fell off the cart and the 'corpse' revived. Some years later she died for real, and this time as the cart approached the corner, her husband cried, 'take care, this is a dangerous corner'. The name stuck.

The good news is that the crossroads is followed by a long descent into the Douglas valley. Of course suspicious minds will be aware that long descents are often followed by equally long climbs. Just before the bottom, you pass a lane to the left which leads to **Appley Bridge** station. The start of the next stage goes straight on up.

ENTWISTLE

As the road climbs away from Chapeltown, there are good views over Wayoh and Entwistle reservoirs before conifers hem the road in. These reservoirs have some popular walks around their shores and are important wildlife havens: around 150 bird species have been sighted in the vicinity of Wayoh reservoir. Entwistle is an excellent place to wait for a train as there is a grand pub, the Strawbury Duck, right next to the station.

RIVINGTON

Descending into Rivington, where Sheep House Lane joins from the right, you join the circuit used for time-trials and road races in the 2002 Commonwealth Games. These produced some great action but – be warned – damp conditions caused problems for several riders on the descent. In the womens' event, Australia's Margaret Hemsley crashed here on the penultimate lap when in a clear lead. A lap later, eventual winner Nicole Cooke of Wales almost ran out of road but was able to re-join the rest of the leading group just before the finish, securing one of the first major wins of a glittering career which included a memorable gold medal in the road race at the Beijing Olympics.

The Commonwealth Games circuit went left at Rivington, through Lever Park. This expanse of woodland, fields and gardens was established by William Hesketh Lever, later Lord Leverhulme, a native of Bolton, who made a fortune from soap and spent much of it in philanthropy. The West Pennine Moors Information Centre is in the Great House Barn, itself a Grade 1 listed building, about 1km down the Lever Park road.

Perhaps the most bizarre feature of the park is the castle. It's shown on OS maps as a 'ruin', but in fact it was built much as it now appears. It is a replica of the now-vanished Liverpool Castle, in the semi-ruined condition in which it stood around the time of Lever Park's foundation in 1900.

113

THE DOUGLAS VALLEY

In the bottom of the valley (explored further by following the Wigan Link, Stage 9a) the River Douglas, Leeds and Liverpool Canal, and Wigan–Southport railway line are all squeezed into a narrow space, which has long been a significant transport route. The river itself was improved in 1742 to facilitate navigation. This was soon supplanted by the Leeds and Liverpool Canal. Established by Act of Parliament in 1770, it reached Wigan in 1781, but wasn't completed through to Leeds until 1816. A major stumbling block was the famous flight of 21 locks just beyond Wigan, more than a fifth of the total number on the entire length. Another notable feature, less than 1km west of Appley Bridge, is a double flight of locks – a sort of dual carriageway of canals.

From its completion in 1816 the canal enjoyed about 30 years of undisputed supremacy before the opening of the nearby railway. In the 20th century it became virtually derelict, until the growth of leisure boating heralded a revival.

STAGE 9A
The Wigan Link

Start	Wigan North Western station SD 581 054
Distance	8.4km/5.2 miles
Total ascent	None: it's all flat or downhill
Ride	Busy streets at start, rough setts on towpath for short way, then better towpath surface
OS maps	Landranger 108 Liverpool
Connections	Wigan North Western station (West Coast Main Line): Wigan Wallgate and Appley Bridge (Wigan–Southport line)
Accommodation	A reasonable, if uninspired, choice of town-centre hotels: otherwise, you'll need to progress well into the next stage

For those arriving by train on the West Coast Main Line, Wigan North Western station (SD 581 054) offers a reasonably convenient connection. You can make the short walk/ride to Wallgate station and get a local train to Appley Bridge, or simply cycle the link.

Follow the towpath of the Leeds and Liverpool Canal (perhaps after taking a look at the Towpath Code: www.canalrivertrust.org.uk/our-towpath-code). For access to this, turn left out of **Wigan North Western** station and keep straight ahead (busy road) for about 250m. At a pedestrian crossing opposite Trencherfield Mill, join the path to the right of the road. Cross a bridge opposite the Orwell and descend to towpath level. Continue past Wigan Pier. The first 100m or so are on bumpy setts, but the surface soon improves. The surroundings aren't always lovely, but they are always interesting, and it all soon becomes more rural. The route is, of course, entirely level, except where it drops a few metres at locks. Join the Cycleway at the first road access after passing under

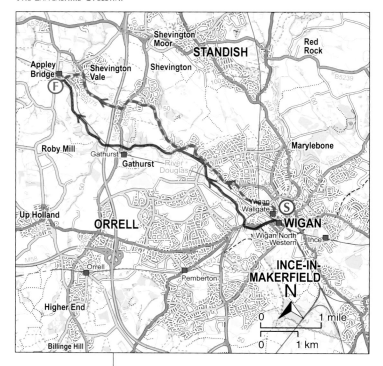

the **M6**, picking up the description at the start of Stage 10 Appley Bridge to Croston.

On-road alternative

If you don't fancy the towpath, presumably because you're on a highly-strung road bike, try this instead: turn right out of Wigan North Western station, then left on King Street West, immediately after Wallgate station. Go left again at a T junction (Dorning Street). After passing the home of Uncle Joe's Mint Balls, turn left again at traffic lights. Follow this road, eventually joining the B5375. Follow this to meet the B5206 at Shevington. Turn left. In about 300m, turn right on New Miles Lane (B5375), signed to Parbold. Cross over the M6 and after about 1.5km turn left on Mill Lane, signed to Appley Bridge station. At a T junction, turn left, joining the Cycleway route.

WIGAN

Wigan was an important market centre long before the Industrial Revolution, having been a borough since the 13th century. Coal was mined in the vicinity, and wool was woven in the town. In 1688 Celia Fiennes described it as 'a pretty market town built of stone and brick,' and there are still many handsome buildings in the town centre.

The construction of the Leeds and Liverpool Canal, which reached Wigan in 1779, precipitated rapid development: the population more than trebled in the first half of the 19th century. However, while the boom brought prosperity for some, it also brought miserable working conditions, poor housing and severe pollution.

Wigan's reputation was blighted, possibly for all time, by the publication in 1937 of George Orwell's *The Road to Wigan Pier*. This remains a classic piece of social reportage, with more than a bit of polemic on the side, but Orwell intended Wigan merely to serve as an example of the dreadful conditions in many industrial towns at the time. He said a few years after, 'it's not worse than fifty other places'.

Looking back at Wigan Pier and Trencherfield Mill

Even before the publication of Orwell's book, Wigan Pier had been something of a music-hall joke. There are two rival explanations for the name: one is that it referred to a wooden gantry once used for loading canal boats, jokingly comparing it to seaside piers like those at Blackpool. The other is that it was simply a wharf like many others on the canals, much like the modern, reconstructed pier just across the canal.

In the 1980s a major restoration project cleaned up and restored much of this area: it was officially unveiled by the Queen in 1985. One of the former warehouses was converted into a large pub/restaurant, named – with or without knowing irony – the Orwell. Sadly, this is currently closed and the area around it is looking distinctly neglected once again. If the link route took you the other way along the canal, you'd see a brighter picture, with the magnificent Trencherfield Mill and recent industrial and office developments flanking the waterway.

On the way out of town the towpath route also passes the DW Stadium. This is shared by Wigan Athletic FC and Wigan Warriors Rugby League FC. Previously known simply as Wigan, the rugby league club is the most successful in the English game, with 20 Championship wins, 19 Challenge Cups and 3 World Club Challenge triumphs. Wigan Athletic has a more modest record but did win the FA Cup in 2013.

STAGE 10
Appley Bridge to Croston

Start	Canal bridge, Appley Bridge SD 523 093
Distance	49.7km/30.9 miles
Total ascent	176m/575ft
Steepest climb	Approx 9% (Bank Brow and Farley Lane)
Ride	Significant gradients over Ashurst's Beacon: roads can be fairly busy, especially at weekends, becoming quieter round Skelmersdale, then busier again just before Croston. After Mere Brow is a section of rough road.
OS maps	Landranger 108 Liverpool: a tiny section on 102 Preston & Blackpool
Connections	Appley Bridge and New Lane on the Wigan–Southport line (connections at Wigan to West Coast Main Line). Town Green (Aughton) and Croston on the Liverpool–Preston line. Services break at Ormskirk, so Town Green is most convenient for Liverpool and Croston for Preston.
Accommodation	Not a tourist area: many pubs on route don't have rooms. Some farmhouse B&Bs: it's wise to book in advance.
Intermediate distances	Town Green station 17.1km/10.6 miles; Heaton's Bridge 29.2km/18.1 miles; Mere Brow 40.5km/25.2 miles

Gazing west from Winter Hill you'd think there was nothing but flat country ahead of you, but this stage starts with a considerable climb, followed by an equally substantial descent. Ashurst's Beacon may seem like a climb too far, but it is a fine viewpoint, and really is the last hill for a long way. As you descend, the rolling and partly wooded landscape gives way to flat and very open country. Fields are large, trees sparse, even hedgerows relatively rare. As the Industrial Revolution transformed the valleys and fringes of the moors further east, a parallel revolution in agriculture was transforming this landscape too.

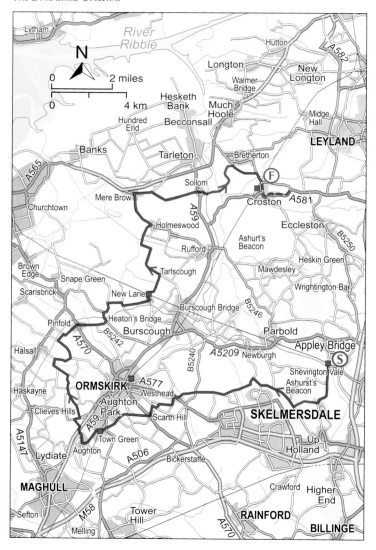

From the canal crossing there's a solid climb of about 2km. As Bank Brow eases into Bank Top, the Star Inn looks incredibly tempting, but it might be better to resist as there's more climbing just ahead, after you turn right into Farley Lane. Twists and turns mean that the climb reveals itself in stages. A sunken lane through woods signifies that it's nearly all over, and finally at a T junction you can turn right and relax: this really is the end of the hard work.

There's a fine view from the roadside here too, south and west over **Skelmersdale** and far beyond, but there's a wider prospect from the Beacon itself, if you don't mind taking a short walk. We'll come to that, but first there's the Prince William Inn: one pub that is in exactly the right place.

The descent is nice and straight to start with but there are two hazards to contend with. One is the inability of some car drivers to comprehend that you may be doing 40 or 50km/h, even when their speedos are telling them so. The other is the sharp right-hander at the bottom, which is followed almost immediately by a left turn.

Follow this road, still descending, to a roundabout. Take the fourth exit, still Beacon Lane, then at a T junction turn left towards Skelmersdale. Just before the next main junction turn right onto a narrow lane and follow it to just before a large roundabout. Avoid this by means of the lane, signed as a cul-de-sac, on the right. At its end walk a few paces then go right on the road. At a T junction turn right into Spa Lane and continue straight ahead at a new roundabout. You have now successfully negotiated (should that be 'avoided'?) the outskirts of Skelmersdale.

At the crossroads by the Plough Inn, go almost straight ahead into Dick's Lane. At the village of **Westhead** turn right onto the **A577** then first left into School Lane. Go first right after 1km into Vicarage Lane. Just after the '30' signs go left on Wellfield Lane, right at its end then first left, up a slight rise past a 'flying-saucer' water-tower.

> On your right here is the campus of **Edge Hill University**. Its origins are as a women's teacher-training college in Liverpool; it relocated to Ormskirk in 1933 and began accepting male students in 1959. It gained full university status in 2006 and was named University of the Year in 2014.

The village feels prosperous and suburban, which is perhaps hardly surprising, with the railway on one side and the A59 on the other connecting it to Liverpool.

Cross the A570, then follow the road round right. After 2km go straight on at a crossroads. Meeting the B5197 on the edge of Town Green, go left then first right into Town Green Lane. Cross over the railway by the station and, if you're not catching a train, continue into **Aughton**. ◄

Turn right at the village green, which has a central cross. Pass the church and up a slight rise to the A59. Cross, probably in two stages, turn right along the dual carriageway then immediately left. Turn right at the end, onto the B5195, then first left into Fir Tree Lane, just before a mini-roundabout. Now go straight ahead for 3km through Clieves Hills.

> Clearly the **definition of a 'hill'** is rather less rigorous on this side of Lancashire, but all things are relative. Compared to the absolute flatness of the drained mosslands which await, this is hilly country.

At a 'Give Way' on a bend turn right, then right again at the next junction, into Asmall Lane. Turn left at the end into Northmoor Lane, then take the next right just before a canal bridge. Go right again at a T junction into Morris Lane and continue to **Pinfold**. Cross the **A570** into Smithy Lane and follow this to a T junction. Turn left onto the

Christmas is coming: Brussels Sprouts growing at Clieves Hills

B5242, cross the canal by the Heaton's Bridge Inn, then take the next right into Drummersdale Lane.

Turn right again into Merscar Lane. This makes a couple of right-angle bends then shadows the canal for a stretch. At a T junction turn left into **New Lane** and over the level crossing just by the station. ▶

This is on the Wigan–Southport line.

At the next T junction turn left on Fish Lane. This leads past the gates of the Wildfowl and Wetlands Trust Centre at Martin Mere (café, toilets). The road continues, with several right-angled bends, for about 4km, to a T junction where it joins the B5246. Go left for another 2km to **Mere Brow**, where the B5246 bends sharp left. There's a shop on the corner where you can get drinks and snacks.

Turn right into Mere Brow Lane. After about 1km turn right on Green Lane, marked 'unsuitable for wide vehicles', just before a large complex of glass-houses. It's bumpy, narrow and sits up above the black, sunken fields alongside. However, romantics who follow cycle-racing (isn't everyone who follows the sport a romantic?) can indulge in the fantasy that they are riding the famous 'Hell of the North' in the classic Paris–Roubaix race.

View from Green Lane towards Tarleton

This is the Rufford branch of the Leeds and Liverpool canal.

There's a slight rise as the lane meets the A59. Go straight across into the tiny village of **Sollom**, turn left then first right, by the post box. Now cross over the canal. ◄

Surprisingly, Preston had no canal connection to the south, while Tarleton was a flourishing seaport. This anomaly was not rectified until 2002, when the **Ribble Link Canal** (see Day Ride 16) connected the Lancaster Canal to the Ribble estuary.

Shortly after the canal bridge there's a fork. A prominent track continues straight ahead but the Cycleway route takes the recently surfaced lane to the left.

Red Bridge takes you over the River Douglas into a quiet lane. At a T junction after a wooded section turn right, then right again into Back Lane, also marked 'No motor vehicles except for access'. Follow this to the T junction where it meets the B5249 and turn right.

The railway bridge just before **Croston** station (Ormskirk–Preston line) is the steepest climb for some time. ▶ Immediately after the bridge, the direct route goes left into Moor Road, by the Temperance Hall. But this misses out on one of Lancashire's most attractive villages.

Detour to Croston

To see Croston properly, at the cost of an extra 1km, keep straight ahead past the station and down to a T junction with the A581. Go left here, through the village centre, then follow the winding road round to a T junction by a large pub (the Highfield). Go right, re-joining the official route.

If you're in need of refreshment, a lane on the right just before the bridge leads to Twin Lakes Velo, a dedicated cycling café.

ASHURST'S BEACON

Just before the start of the descent, there are several footpaths leading off right. Any of these will lead, in about 300 metres, to the Beacon itself. This was built during the Napoleonic Wars, when most people feared that a French invasion was imminent. Before the invention of the telegraph, beacons were the fastest way to spread news, though bandwidth was extremely limited. There's also a view indicator nearby.

The view lacks something in foreground – the hill is too flat-topped for that – but nothing in extent. To the east is Winter Hill. Runcorn Bridge is a landmark to seek out, about 25km due south; a little to its right and further off are the sandstone scarps of Frodsham and Helsby and the industrial complexes around the Mersey. South-west is Liverpool, with its two cathedrals, and beyond that the Wirral and then the Clwydian Hills. On a good day, much further west, you may see Snowdonia.

Turning to the north, Blackpool Tower seems to be what most people look for, but it's the Lakeland skyline that really lifts the heart. And then there are the Bowland Fells, and the Anglezarke moors, and we're back to Winter Hill.

WEST LANCASHIRE'S FENS

The drained mosslands seem like easy travelling country to us today, but this wasn't always the case. Ancient tracks and roads typically followed high ground because it made for easier journeys. Lowlands were often swampy, densely wooded, or both. Large-scale drainage schemes in the late 18th and early 19th centuries produced extraordinary transformations in these landscapes. The 'useless' mosslands of west Lancashire became rich farmlands that fed the growing industrial towns further east.

There was once a large lake around Martin Mere, much larger than the present-day reserve and probably the largest in Lancashire. The 'mere' of Mere Brow is the same Martin Mere, which gives you some idea of the former extent of the lake. Local legend maintains that this was the lake into which King Arthur hurled Excalibur, but many places make similar claims.

You will need to visit the centre and walk around the reserve to see what the surviving mossland looks like, but you may well get an idea of its wider importance merely by cycling past. This is particularly true in winter, when massive flocks of migrant birds gather on surrounding fields, which are often partly flooded. Dominant among these are thousands of pink-footed geese.

CROSTON

From the official route Croston doesn't seem all that special, but the suggested detour reveals its charms. The view of the packhorse bridge over the tiny River Yarrow, with the tower of St Michael and All Angels Church rising over the rooftops behind, must be one of the most photographed in Lancashire.

Croston

The packhorse bridge dates from 1682; the church boasts a history stretching back to 1075. Nearby Church Street, especially if you can get a clear view without too many cars, also displays much period character, with a number of houses dated to 1704. Perhaps we should also mention that there are several good pubs in the village.

STAGE 11
Croston to Whalley

Start	Croston station SD 486 193
Distance	42.6km/26.5 miles
Total ascent	400m/1310ft
Steepest climb	Approx 15% (Samlesbury Bottoms)
Ride	Lanes, suburban roads then a fairly busy link road, but soon the ride is on secluded lanes again. Constant undulations and a couple of distinct but not monstrous climbs
OS maps	Landranger 108 Liverpool; 102 Preston & Blackpool; 103 Blackburn & Burnley
Connections	Croston for Preston & Ormskirk (connections to Liverpool). Leyland, on the West Coast Main line, has local trains only. Wilpshire and Whalley for the Manchester–Clitheroe line: change at Blackburn for Preston. Buckshaw Parkway is on the Preston–Manchester line.
Accommodation	Not a particularly tourist-orientated area, but there's a reasonable spread of the usual pubs and B&Bs
Intermediate distances	Leyland (railway bridge) 9.8km/6.1 miles; Brindle 19.8km/12.3 miles; Mellor 31.4km/19.5 miles

Even in the busiest town centre in Lancashire you're rarely far from real countryside. This fact is borne out frequently along the Cycleway, but never better than on this stage. After a gently rural start, the route skirts Leyland's suburban fringe and the new community of Buckshaw Village. By the time you reach Whittle-le-Woods you're heading out into green country again.

Now the route has to find a way between Preston and Blackburn, at the very heart of urban Lancashire. Or so you might think. Motorways and main roads are crossed, but the route sticks to minor roads and lanes. Only from the hill crests do you get any real sense of the proximity of the urban scene, and between them are some real hidden nooks and crannies. There's a bigger climb around Mellor, with bigger views, and the last few kilometres give you a sense of returning to the hill country.

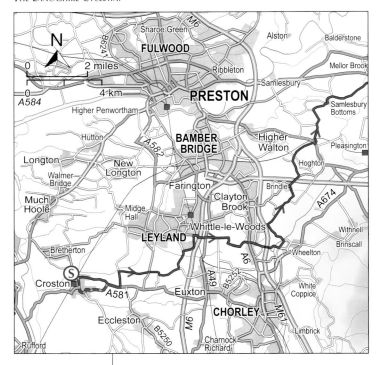

Map continued
on page 130

Here it feels as if
you're heading
straight back towards
Winter Hill.

The two alternative routes at Croston reunite at the T junction by the Highfield pub. Follow the **A581** eastward for about 1km then go left on Ulnes Walton Lane. Just before the bridge over the River Lostock make a sharp right on narrow Holker Lane, marked 'Unsuitable for HGV'. Follow this to a T junction with the B5253.

Go right for 50 metres then left into Flag Lane. ◀ At a T junction go left, joining a wider road, and follow it past the Plough Inn before going left into Runshaw Hall Lane. There's a dip and rise, nothing much in itself but enough to signal the end of the flatlands. Just after this go right into Langdale Road and follow it past Runshaw College and into a brief suburban interlude.

At the end meet the B5248 at a mini-roundabout. Go right, over the railway, straight on at another mini-roundabout, then over the M6 to meet the A49 at traffic lights. Follow the cycle-lane markings, which direct you as if turning right but then lead across to a cycle path alongside the road opposite (Dawson Lane). This leads to a roundabout with a large sculpture. Follow the cycle signs into the continuation of Dawson Lane (signed for Whittle-le-Woods), then join the road.

As the main road now goes through Buckshaw Village, Dawson Lane actually seems quieter than it

On the outskirts of Buckshaw Village

This is easy to overshoot, especially as several Cycleway signs seem to be missing in this area. ◄

used to. Follow it through several pronounced bends to its end at the **A6**. Go right for 100m then first left into Shaw Brow on the outskirts of **Whittle-le-Woods**. The first decent freewheel since Ashurst's Beacon is followed by a swing right, then a right turn into Town Lane, with a sign 'Heapey 2'. ◄

After the first freewheel since Ashurst's Beacon, the first climb. The road ducks under the M61 and continues climbing to a canal bridge at Johnson's Hillock Locks. Climb a bit more then go left into Copthurst Lane, which first climbs then descends to re-cross the canal by the Top Lock pub.

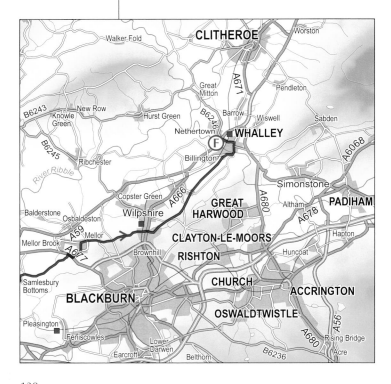

Officially the **Cycleway carries on** up Town Lane, then bears left onto Blackburn Road, then left again on Kenyon Lane opposite the Red Lion in Wheelton village. This involves extra distance, extra climbing and busier roads. It seems pretty pointless to me but if you're a completist this is the way to go.

Johnson's Hillock Locks

Cross the bridge by the Top Lock and descend fairly steeply. A sharp bend hides the next climb, after which the road comes very close to the M61. Go right and climb – not too steeply – to the top of Hough Hill. Drop down into **Brindle** and go right on the B5256. ▶

St James's Church stands just by the junction.

Follow the B5256 for about 1km. Soon after passing over the M65 go left into Hillhouse Lane, where there's a sign for Gregson Lane. Gregson Lane is actually a substantial village, but you'll see nothing of it.

A nice twisting descent follows, with views north to the Bowland Fells and west to Preston. As the gradient eases turn right. It's signed 'R C Church', and also marked 'Private Road', but fear not. Follow this, almost parallel to the Preston–Blackburn railway line. At the

131

end, entering the village of **Hoghton**, turn right, then right again on the A675. After 100m go left by the Boar's Head into Gib Lane.

Dip under the railway, climb a bit, then take the next right, Goosefoot Lane. After about 1km keep right then make a short, tricky descent into **Samlesbury Bottoms** with its former cotton mill. Climb out equally steeply then at Nab's Head turn right into Further Lane. ◄ Follow this to its end and turn right onto the **A677**.

The pub from which the hamlet takes its name is just to the left at this junction.

This is the most direct road between Preston and Blackburn, and as such it's always busy. The good news is that you only follow it for 200m. The bad news is that as soon as you turn left into the lane for **Mellor** the climbing starts again. There's a brief level interlude passing the post office and church before a right turn at a T junction begins another steady climb: official maps seem to suggest you turn right earlier, but the signs take you this way.

A snowy Pendle Hill, the Pennines beyond, from Top of Ramsgreave

Level off around Top of Ramsgreave then sweep down the flank of the ridge to **Ramsgreave and Wilpshire** station. At traffic lights go straight across and

into another climb. As it eases, with Parsonage Reservoir on the right, bear left onto York Road, with a sign 'Whalley 3½'. At the next T junction bear left. There's just a short rise to the crest, a great view of the Ribble Valley, and then a superb descent through York village. This shows Lancashire folk are broad-minded: there isn't a Lancaster in Yorkshire!

Watch out for the speed bumps coming into **Billington** and watch out even more for the vicious hairpin at the bottom. Just below this turn right and down into **Whalley**. For the railway station go straight on past all the shops then turn left.

LEYLAND

You don't really see anything of the town of Leyland. Once a major car-manufacturing centre, today it concentrates mostly on commercial vehicles and is home to the British Commercial Vehicle Museum. It also has one of the highest concentrations of bike shops per head of population in Lancashire.

There has been major development here, both industrial and residential, on the former Royal Ordnance Works site, now known as Buckshaw Village. There's even a new railway station, Buckshaw Parkway.

HOGHTON TOWER

The route passes within about 1km of Hoghton Tower, but you never really see it. This 16th-century hilltop manor house is one of the best-known houses in Lancashire. Painstakingly restored in the 19th century, it has been used several times for film location shooting. Another claim to fame is the story, endlessly repeated, that here in 1617 James I knighted a particularly fine joint of beef. It has been sirloin ('Sir Loin') ever since.

MELLOR MOOR

The pub by the T junction in Mellor is called the Millstone (*Good Pub Guide* recommended). The name may seem cruelly apt, especially if there's an easterly wind blowing. However as the gradient eases you realise that the road is following the spine of a distinct ridge, which gives sweeping views: the crest of Mellor Moor was the site of a Roman signalling station. On the left are the Bowland Fells, Ribble Valley and Pendle Hill. Then, as the road levels off at Ramsgreave, there's also a view down to the right to Blackburn, seemingly ringed by hills. This is as close as the Cycleway gets to Blackburn, and your only real view of it. Although city status was conferred on Preston as part of the Queen's Jubilee celebrations in 2002, the county's cathedral is in Blackburn.

DAY RIDES

Sportive rider approaching Bowland Knotts, Pendle Hill in the distance (Day Ride 5)

INTRODUCTION

The Cycleway route is designed to cover the length and breadth of Lancashire on the best roads for cycling. It isn't specifically designed for the benefit of those who would prefer to tackle it in sections. The information given in this book about connections will help, but you won't always get the best rides by focusing exclusively on the Cycleway.

What follows is a series of suggested day rides, mostly around 45km (30 miles), which will allow you to 'tick off' sections of the Cycleway but also incorporate other enjoyable roads. These routes are conceived to be convenient for access by train: they either connect two stations on the same line, or return to the starting point (these circular rides are, of course, also convenient for access by car).

These brief descriptions are intended to be followed with the aid of appropriate Landranger maps.

DAY RIDE 1

Lancaster–Silverdale one-way

Start	Lancaster station SD 472 617
Finish	Silverdale station SD 476 751
Distance	22km/13.7 miles
Total ascent	140m/460ft
Ride	Gently hilly
See also	Stage 1a, Stage 1

After an urban (but traffic-free) opening, this is essentially a fairly gentle ride through rolling country, though it does climb high enough to earn some far-reaching views. There's another brief but interesting urban section in Carnforth, then it's lush and easy again.

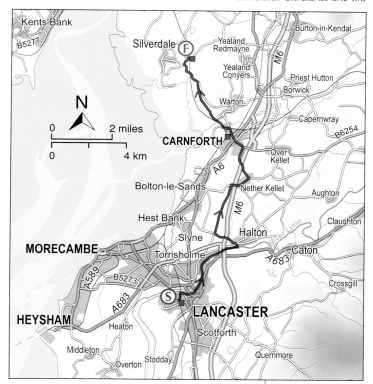

Leave Lancaster station by gate alongside Platform 1 and follow the cycle path to the right. At road, go under the railway and turn left on the cycle path, soon joining an old railway. Ride past the Millennium Bridge and through an underpass. Continue on the cycle path under the M6 then cross the river at **Halton**. Turn left at a T junction then straight ahead into Foundry Lane.

Cross over the M6 then turn right. At the next T junction turn right again, through **Nether Kellet**. Near top of village turn left

137

for Carnforth. Turn left at T junction onto the B6254 and down into **Carnforth**. Go straight ahead at traffic lights. Pass Carnforth station, go over one railway bridge, then under a second and turn left. Cross the River Keer by a wooden bridge. At the end of the lane turn right, then left on a wider road. After a level crossing turn right, with care, for **Silverdale** station.

DAY RIDE 2
Lancaster–Silverdale–Lancaster

Start/finish	Lancaster station SD 472 617
Distance	54.5km/33.9 miles
Total ascent	478m/1570ft
Ride	Moderately hilly
See also	Stage 1a, Stage 1, short section of Stage 6

The first half is the same as the previous ride, but the route peels off just before Silverdale station and, after exploring more of the Arnside–Silverdale AONB, finds a different but equally attractive return to Lancaster.

Leave Lancaster station by gate alongside Platform 1 and follow the cycle path to the right. At road, go under the railway and turn left on the cycle path, soon joining an old railway. Ride past the Millennium Bridge and through an underpass. Continue on the cycle path under the M6 then cross the river at **Halton**. Turn left at a T junction then straight ahead into Foundry Lane.

Cross over the M6 then turn right. At the next T junction turn right again, through **Nether Kellet**. Near top of village turn left for Carnforth. Turn left at T junction onto the B6254 and down into **Carnforth**. Go straight ahead at traffic lights. Pass Carnforth station, go over one railway bridge, then under a second and turn left. Cross the River

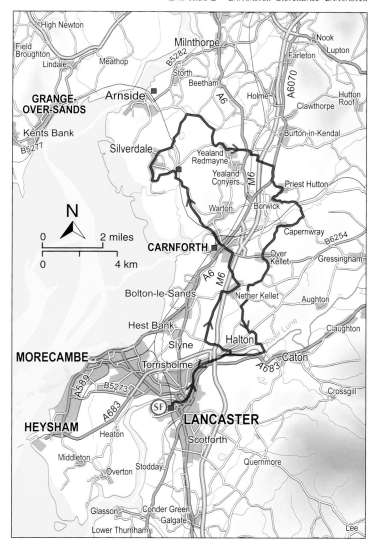

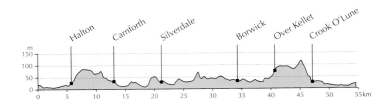

Keer by a wooden bridge. At the end of the lane turn right, then left on a wider road. After a level crossing turn left then left again onto Hollins Lane. Keep right at Wolf House Gallery, then right again and up to a T junction. Turn left, through **Silverdale** village, eventually swinging right. At the next T junction turn left.

Keep right past a junction with the Cumbria Cycleway at a turning for Arnside. Keep straight ahead until the road climbs then drops sharply to T junction.

Descending towards Crook O'Lune, with Clougha Pike on the horizon

Turn left and ride into **Yealand Redmayne**. Turn left (the turnoff is quite well hidden) on Eight Acre Lane, signposted to Milnthorpe and Kendal. Go straight across the A6 into Tarn Lane. Turn right then left, cross over the

railway, motorway and canal, and continue to the A6070. Turn right then first left, signposted to **Priest Hutton**.

Keep right and follow the lane towards **Borwick**. At the village green bear left, signposted Capernwray and Arkholme. Cross over the railway, keep straight ahead for 1km then turn right through **Capernwray** to **Over Kellet** and straight ahead at the village green, signed to Nether Kellet. Turn left opposite Hawthorns Caravan Park, pass between quarries and follow the road south, ignoring side turnings. Descend to a T junction. Turn left then first right (signed for Caton). At the bottom turn left and ride down to the **River Lune** at Crook O'Lune. From the car park here follow the cycle track back to Lancaster.

DAY RIDE 3
Lancaster–High Bentham

Start	Lancaster station SD 472 617
Finish	Bentham station SD 667 689
Distance	44km/27.4 miles
Total ascent	628m/2060ft
Ride	Continuously hilly, but no monster climbs
See also	Stage 1a, Stage 1, Stage 2

A most attractive route, the lumpy terrain giving endless variety in ride and surroundings. It does, however, require a little forward planning, as return trains from High Bentham are at least two hours apart.

Leave Lancaster station by gate alongside Platform 1 and follow the cycle path to the right. At road, go under the railway and turn left on the cycle path, soon joining an old railway. Ride past the Millennium Bridge and through an underpass. Continue on the cycle path under the M6

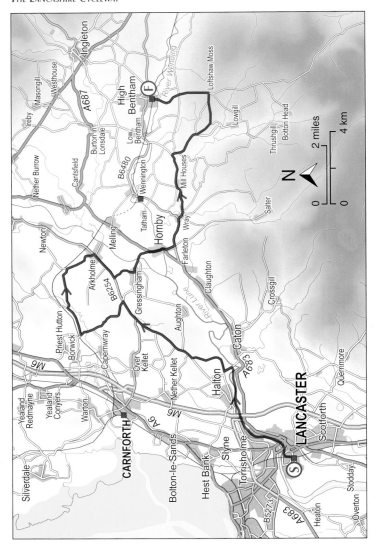

but don't cross the river at **Halton**: instead keep straight ahead to Crook O'Lune.

Exit the car park and turn right, then right again. Climb past Halton Park then turn right on wider road which climbs onto a ridge. ▶ Turn right on the B6254 then first left. Climb then descend past Capernwray Hall. Just before the railway turn right and follow the road through a valley, over a short climb then down to a T junction.

There are fine views from the ridge.

Turn right, and soon descend to **Arkholme**. Turn right on the **B6254** then first left, signposted to **Gressingham**. In the village turn left, and left again at a T junction. Cross Loyn Bridge and continue to the A683. Turn right and descend into **Hornby**.

At the end of Main Street, where the main road goes right, keep straight ahead onto Station Road. At the crossroads at Butt Yeats turn left on the B6480 to **Wray**. Turn right on Main Street, follow the road past Bridge House Farm and continue past Mill Houses. After a sharp climb the road follows a little ridge.

Go right, signposted to Lowgill, and continue 2km to a triple junction. Keep straight ahead, signposted Slaidburn and Burnmoor. Continue onto open moor and at T junction turn left to descend to **High Bentham** and Bentham station.

DAY RIDE 4
Lancaster–High Bentham–Lancaster

Start/finish	Lancaster station SD 472 617
Distance	74.1km/46 miles
Total ascent	855m/2805ft
Ride	Continuously hilly
See also	Stage 1a, Stage 1, Stage 2, Stage 6

This makes a good circuit and avoids having to wait for the very infrequent trains on the Lancaster–Leeds line. The first part of the ride is the same as Day Ride 3.

Leave Lancaster station by gate alongside Platform 1 and follow the cycle path to the right. At road, go under the railway and turn left on the cycle path, soon joining an old railway. Ride past the Millennium Bridge and through an underpass. Continue on the cycle path under the M6 but don't cross the river at **Halton**: instead keep straight ahead to Crook O'Lune.

Exit the car park and turn right, then right again. Climb past Halton Park then turn right on wider road which climbs onto a ridge. ◄ Turn right on the B6254 then first left. Climb then descend past Capernwray Hall. Just before the railway turn right and follow the road through a valley, over a short climb then down to a T junction.

There are fine views from the ridge.

Turn right, and soon descend to **Arkholme**. Turn right on the **B6254** then first left, signposted to **Gressingham**. In the village turn left, and left again at a T junction. Cross Loyn Bridge and continue to the A683. Turn right and descend into **Hornby**.

At the end of Main Street, where the main road goes right, keep straight ahead onto Station Road. At the

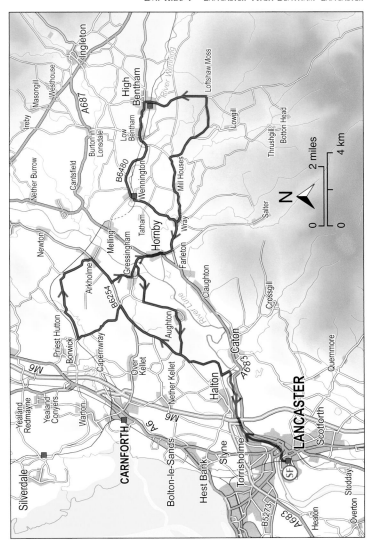

crossroads at Butt Yeats turn left on the B6480 to **Wray**. Turn right on Main Street, follow the road past Bridge House Farm and continue past Mill Houses. After a sharp climb the road follows a little ridge.

Descending towards Halton Park

Go right, signposted to Lowgill, and continue 2km to a triple junction. Keep straight ahead, signposted Slaidburn and Burnmoor. Continue onto open moor and at T junction turn left to descend to **High Bentham** and Bentham station.

From High Bentham the simplest/short-est route back is along the B6480 to join the A683 just west of Hornby. A more interesting – and much quieter – alternative follows the B6480 to the crossroad at Butt Yeats, south of Hornby, then backtracks along the Cycleway route to Loyn Bridge: turn right at the crossroads, then straight ahead onto **Hornby**'s Main Street. At Hornby's far end bear left onto Fleet Lane, cross Loyn Bridge.

After the bridge take the first left. Go left at a T junction then fork right. Turn left on a wider road. ▶ At a T junction turn left and left again to descend past Halton Park to Crook O'Lune. Follow the cycle track back to Lancaster.

Here are great views above Aughton.

DAY RIDE 5
High Bentham–Slaidburn–High Bentham

Start/finish	Bentham station SD 667 689
Distance	45.8km/28.4 miles
Total ascent	922m/3025ft
Ride	Extremely hilly
See also	Stage 2, Stage 3

This is a tough circuit, but on a clear day it is staggeringly beautiful and sheer inspiration should keep you going.

Turn right (south) from Bentham station, climbing virtu-ally all the way, to **Cross O'Greet**. Continue down, up over **Merrybent Hill** and down again to **Slaidburn**. Turn left at the war memorial, and follow the B6478; where the Cycleway route goes right, stay on the B6478 for another 3km to a crossroads then turn left, signposted to

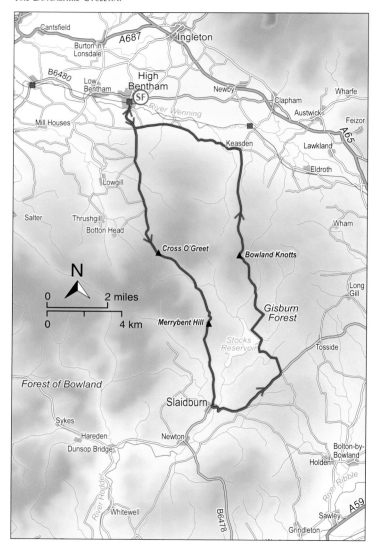

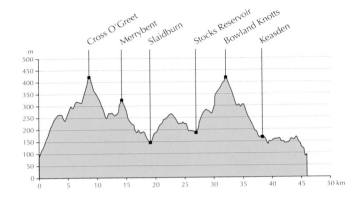

Gisburn Forest. Follow road over Bowland Knotts then long descent to crossroads at **Keasden**. Turn left and continue to a crossroads and the junction with outward route. Turn right, back down into **Bentham**.

Sportive rider near the top on Bowland Knotts

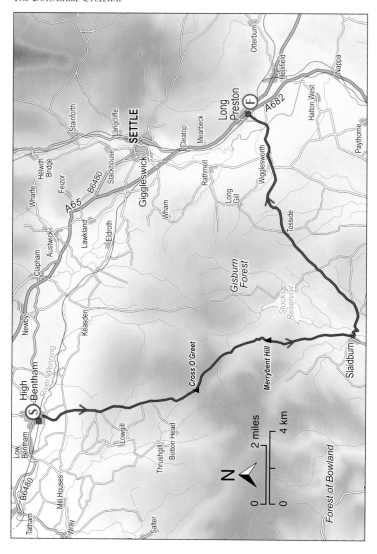

DAY RIDE 6

High Bentham–Long Preston

Start	Bentham station SD 667 689
Finish	Long Preston station SD 833 579
Distance	34.5km/21.4 miles
Total ascent	648m/2125ft
Ride	Very hilly
See also	Stage 2, Stage 3

This route allows you to tick off Cross O'Greet without the monster return leg over Bowland Knotts. Even so, it's hardly a stroll in the park and is still best saved for a good day.

Turn right (south) from Bentham station, climbing virtually all the way, to **Cross O'Greet**. Continue down, up over **Merrybent Hill** and down again to **Slaidburn**. Then stay on B6478 all the way to **Long Preston**.

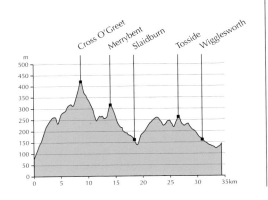

DAY RIDE 7

Clitheroe–Slaidburn–Clitheroe

Start/finish	Clitheroe station SD 741 420
Distance	41km/25.5 miles
Total ascent	586m/1925ft
Ride	Hilly
See also	Stage 3

This circuit may be modest in distance, but it packs a lot in. The Marl Hill climb is a tough one, but there's very little traffic to intrude on your struggle, and it's repaid soon enough as the views are magnificent. Watch the descent, though. The rest of the ride is less intense but still gorgeous.

Clitheroe Castle

Exit Platform 1 and turn left (from Platform 2, go under the underpass then turn left). Turn left on the B6478 to **Waddington**.

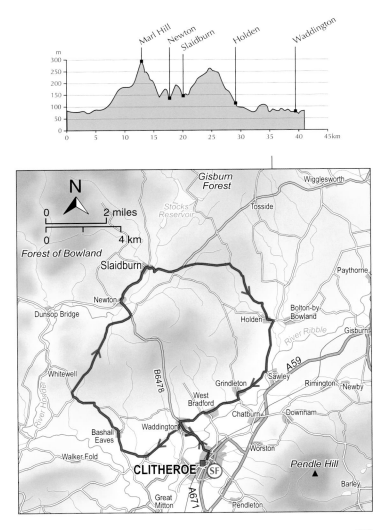

Turn left just after the church to join the Cycleway route. After Bashall Barn turn right. Ride through Bashall Eaves and past Browsholme Hall then at Cow Ark turn right (signed Whitewell) then right again (signed Newton). Climb over Marl Hill. ◄ Re-join the B6478, turn left to **Newton** and continue through **Slaidburn**.

Cross the river and make a sharp climb, then take the second right, where the B6478 veers left. At T junction turn right for long descent into **Holden**. Keep left in the village and continue to a T junction by the Copy Nook pub. Turn right, then right again at wide junction just before **Sawley**, signposted to Slaidburn, Waddington, West Bradford and Grindleton. Follow the road's twisting descent through **Grindleton**, and continue through **West Bradford** back to **Waddington**. At a T junction at the upper end of Waddington turn left on the B6478 back to **Clitheroe**.

Beware of horrendous road surfaces on the main descents.

DAY RIDE 8

A circuit from Whalley

Start/finish	Whalley station SD 729 364
Distance	29.7km/18.5 miles
Total ascent	290m/950ft
Ride	Moderately hilly
See also	Stage 3, Stage 7

'Short and sweet' may be a cliché, but it aptly describes this classic circuit around the heart of the Ribble Valley.

From Whalley station turn left then left again at a mini-roundabout. After 400m turn right on Wiswell Lane. Cross the A681 and keep right, skirting **Wiswell** village (signposted for Pendleton). In **Pendleton** turn right and

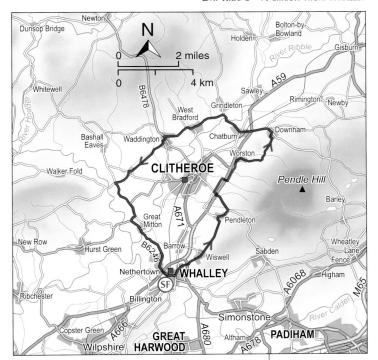

continue to T junction near Pendleton Hall. Turn left and descend to the A59. Cross via refuges into the lane opposite and after 100m turn right again onto a lane marked as a dead end 'Except cycles'. Follow this, then re-cross the A59, continue on the cycle track on the other side then join the lane into **Worston**. Turn right, ride through the village and continue to **Downham**.

Turn left, then climb to a church and pub and keep left. Continue into **Chatburn**. Turn left on the main road then right

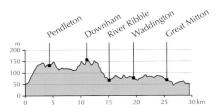

just after the post office into Ribble Lane. Cross the river then turn left on the outskirts of **Grindleton**. Continue through **West Bradford** to **Waddington**. At the T junction at the upper end of village turn left then shortly right, before the church. Continue along Twitter Lane to a T junction after Bashall Barn. Turn left, then very soon turn right. At a crossroads turn left and at the next junction turn right onto the B6243. After 1km turn left on the B6246 through **Great Mitton** and back into **Whalley**.

DAY RIDE 9
A circuit from Colne

Start/finish	Colne station SD 881 398
Distance	47.4km/29.5 miles
Total ascent	1016m/3335ft
Ride	Very hilly
See also	Stage 7, Stage 8

Another tough ride, best saved for a clear day, when it is wonderfully scenic.

From the station turn left then 2nd left on Queen St (signposted Ring Road, Skipton, Keighley). Go straight ahead at the traffic lights then follow the B6247 to **Barrowford**. Turn left on Main Street (A682) then right just before White Bear pub, signposted Roughlee. After steep climb continue over ridge and down to **Roughlee**. Turn left at a T junction then right at a crossroads to **Barley**. In Barley turn right at T junction signposted Downham.

Climb over the shoulder of Pendle Hill to a crossroads and turn left to **Downham**. Turn right at the top of the hill in Downham, by the post office. Keep straight ahead, ignoring side turnings, and continue along a narrow gated lane. Cross the A682 and follow Stocks Lane. At a crossroads

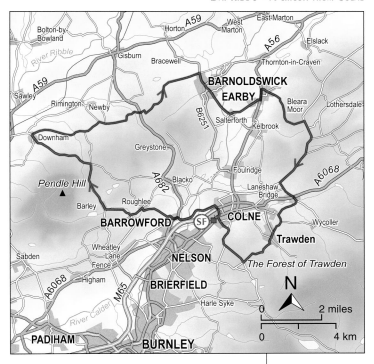

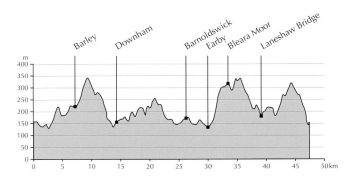

157

turn right on the B6251 into **Barnoldswick**. Keep virtually straight ahead through town, joining the B6383.

Continue into **Salterforth**, turn left at a crossroads and follow a lane (Earby Road). At a T junction turn left on the A56 then fork right by a Co-operative food store into Victoria Road, signposted Lothersdale. At a mini-roundabout take the 3rd exit, Water Street. Keep right on Stoney Bank Road to climb over **Bleara Moor**.

At a T junction turn right, descend, climb and descend again. At the bottom turn left into Long Lane then at T junction down Emmott Lane to **Laneshaw Bridge**. Turn left on **A6068** then instantly right into School Lane. After a bridge turn right again on Carriers Row. Go left at T junction, then keep right and descend into **Trawden**.

At T junction, turn left. Turn right below church, then immediately left on Burnley Road. Climb, with a brief dip in the middle, to a crossroads by Clarion House, and turn right, signposted Colne. A great descent follows, all the way into **Colne**, meeting the A682 just 50m from the station entrance.

DAY RIDE 10

Colne–Accrington

Start	Colne station SD 881 398
Finish	Accrington station SD 757 285
Distance	38.7km/24 miles
Total ascent	685m/2245ft
Ride	Very hilly
See also	Stage 8

A pretty tough ride; the distance may be modest but there's hardly any flat road. The climbing starts immediately and there's no easy way to do a warm-up on the train.

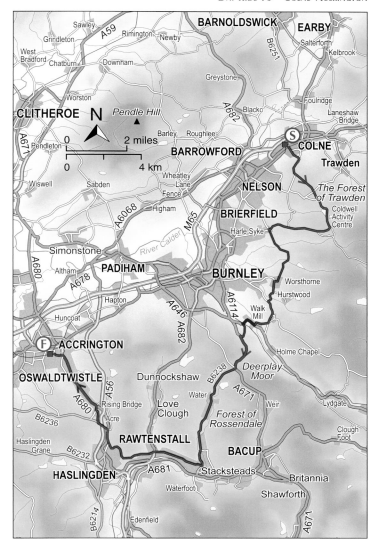

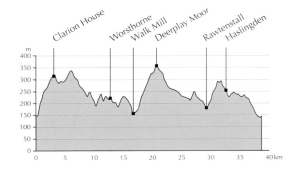

Here there is
a tearoom.

From the station turn left then 1st right on Bridge St. A long climb soon follows to Clarion House crossroads. Go straight ahead, signposted Coldwell and Hebden Bridge, and descend to **Coldwell Activity Centre**. ◀

The road wriggles round the reservoir and climbs a bit more: after 1km keep right (past a pillbox). Now make long descent through Lane Bottom and up to a crossroads in Haggate. Turn left and continue to **Worsthorne**. Keep straight ahead, just right of the village store. In 1km climb to a T junction and turn left on a wider road.

Descend to Over Town and turn right on Mount Lane for steep descent with hairpin at bottom. At T junction turn right on the A646. Go under railway then turn left on narrow lane signed as a dead end 'Except cycles'. Climb to a T junction, turn right to the A671, turn left and after a long, steady climb turn right onto the **B6238**, signposted to Rawtenstall.

Descend through **Water**, Lumb and Whitewell Bottom. Just after some old mills on the left, turn right on a street called Bridleway. Climb to a T junction, then turn right on Turnpike and keep climbing. Continue more easily and descend into **Rawtenstall**.

At traffic lights go (almost) straight ahead into Haslingden Old Road. After a steady climb contour round then descend into **Haslingden**. On a sweeping left bend turn right onto High St. Follow this up then down to

The cycle track into Accrington

the **A680**, then almost straight across into Hud Hey Road. Keep left and climb to cross over the A56, then right into Rising Bridge Road.

Re-join the A680 and turn left. Follow this down into **Accrington**. In the town centre bear left on Abbey St, then turn left on Blackburn Rd and left on Eagle St to the station.

Or, more pleasantly, just after Holland's pie factory, turn left down a narrow lane before a bus stop to find a cycle track which takes you down the valley. At the end turn right and cross the mini-roundabout into Eagle St. The station is just after Tesco, on the left.

DAY RIDE 11

Entwistle–Haslingden–Ramsbottom–Entwistle

Start/finish	Entwistle station SD 727 176
Distance	33.3km/20.7 miles
Total ascent	500m/1640ft
Ride	Moderately hilly
See also	Stage 8, Stage 9

A slightly odd route, but fun, and it covers bits of the cycleway which aren't readily accessible by train otherwise.

From Entwistle station descend the lane and cross a causeway over Wayoh Reservoir. Come up to T junction, turn left, then next right (Moorside Rd). At the next T junction turn left and follow the (very scenic) road north to a T junction by the Grey Mare pub. Turn right (**B6232**), climb a bit more, then speed down Grane valley towards **Haslingden**. Turn right on the B5235, signposted Helmshore (if you've a fetish to cycle the whole Cycleway you'll have to do a short return leg into the town centre here.)

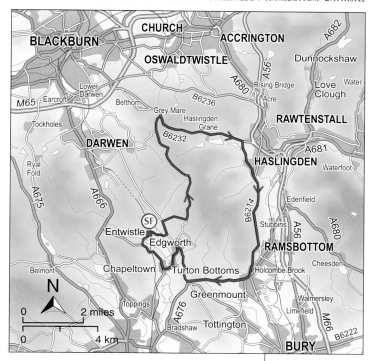

From a junction follow the B5235 to **Holcombe Brook** and a T junction with the A676. Turn right and through traffic lights. After a short climb continue through Hawkshaw and past small Walves reservoir. At a crossroads just above, turn right – easy to miss –signposted Edgworth Entwistle.

Continue to a crossroads in **Edgworth**. Turn left, down into **Turton Bottoms**, then up again and turn sharp right into **Chapeltown** High Street. Continue through Chapeltown and onto the moors, then cross over a railway. Turn right on Batridge Road to return to Entwistle station.

After the ride, the best place to wait for the next train is in **The Strawbury Duck** (yes, that is how it's spelled). Even if it were not so close to the trains, it would be a great pub, but its location makes it outstanding. Maybe the train after next…

The short leg of the Cycleway **from the Batridge Road turnoff above Entwistle to Belmont** is hard to fit into a suitable circuit, especially as the A666 is not the pleasantest road to cycle on. If you're completing the Cycleway in stages the best way to tick off this section is as a short out-and-back (15.6km/9.7 miles) which can be tagged onto the above.

DAY RIDE 12

A circuit from Leyland

Start/finish	Leyland station SD 547 227
Distance	54.4km/33.8 miles
Total ascent	449m/1475ft
Ride	Moderately hilly
See also	Stage 11, Stage 9

This ride is busier, in parts, than most of its counterparts, but that's inescapable; without taking to a mountain bike, there aren't too many options around the West Pennine Moors. On the plus side, it's got plenty to keep you interested and the high crossing to Rivington contrasts well with gentler, rolling terrain elsewhere.

It may be easier just to walk across the bridge.

From the station exit turn right, cross a bridge then turn right again at a mini-roundabout into Moss Lane. ◄ After the church turn right on Bow Lane and follow it around to end at a T junction. Turn right then left into Ryden Ave. Continue straight ahead to the end, then turn right on

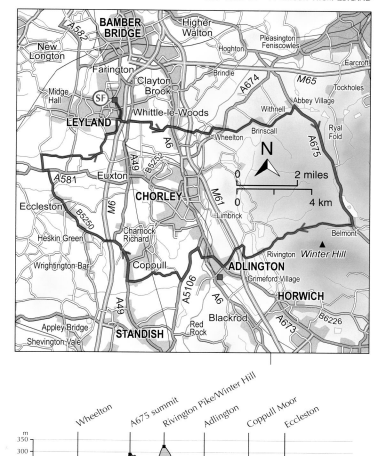

Beaumaris Rd and left to a mini-roundabout beside a railway bridge. Turn left (joining the Cycleway route).

Continue over the M6 and meet the A49 at traffic lights. Follow cycle lane markings to a cycle path alongside the road opposite (Dawson Lane), then to a roundabout with a large sculpture. Follow the continuation of Dawson Lane, signposted Whittle-le-Woods, to meet the **A6**. Go right then 1st left into Shaw Brow. Descend, then turn right into Town Lane, signposted 'Heapey 2'. ◀

Climb under the M61, up to a canal bridge at Johnson's Hillock Locks and on up Town Lane. At the top, by a school, bear left on Blackburn Road into **Wheelton** village. Follow the road round to the right (Victoria St) to the A674. Go straight across, past the Dressers Arms. At a crossroads by a school turn right into **Brinscall**. Where main road swings left keep straight ahead (past weight limit signs) for the climb of Butterworth Brow. Turn right at a T junction then down to the A675. Turn right.

Follow the **A675** for about 7km, first climbing gradually then descending into **Belmont**. Turn right on Church St by the Black Bull pub. Climb gradually over moors then make a fine, long descent to **Rivington**. At the village green turn right.

Cross Rivington Reservoir dam and at a T junction turn right. Follow the road round and over the M61. Go left by the Bay Horse Inn and down into **Adlington**.

At the traffic lights turn right on the A673 then left by the White Horse pub into Rawlinson Lane. Go straight across the A6 then continue to a T junction with the **A5106**. Go left for about 3km, then turn right into Jolly Tar Lane. At the next pub, the Waggon and Horses, turn left to reach a T junction on the **A49**. Turn right then continue for 2.5km to a roundabout and turn left, signposted Eccleston. Cross over the **M6** then keep right along Park Hill Rd. At a T junction turn right on the **B5250** and continue through **Heskin Green** and **Eccleston**. Turn left on New Lane.

At a T junction turn left on the **A581**, then right on Ulnes Walton Lane. Just before a bridge turn sharp right on Holker Lane. At a T junction with the B5253,

Cycleway signs are missing in this area.

go right for 50m then left into Flag Lane. At a T junction turn left, pass the Plough Inn then turn left into Runshaw Hall Lane. Turn right into Langdale Road and follow past Runshaw College. Meet the B5248 at a mini-roundabout and go right, over the railway, then left into Bent Lane. Retrace the outward route to the station.

DAY RIDE 13
A West Lancashire circuit

Start/finish	Appley Bridge station SD 524 093
Distance	65.2km/40.5 miles
Total ascent	449m/1475ft
Ride	Gently hilly
See also	Stage 10, Stage 11, Stage 9

This loop could equally well be started at Town Green, New Lane or Croston, according to convenience. It can also be split into two halves: either Appley Bridge–New Lane–Appley Bridge, or Town Green–Croston–Town Green (in this latter case you'll need to change trains at Ormskirk, or make a short extra ride from Ormskirk to Town Green). However, since it's relatively gentle terrain overall, and since there are stations spaced around the loop, it's a relatively non-committing way to see if you can ride 65km (40.5 miles) in a day.

From the canal climb to Bank Top. Soon turn right into Farley Lane. Climb again to a T junction and turn right along the ridge of Ashurst's Beacon. Descend to a sharp right hand bend then turn left opposite Dalton church. Continue to a roundabout. Take the 4th exit, Beacon Lane, then at a T junction turn left towards **Skelmersdale**. Just before the next large junction turn right on a narrow lane and follow this to its end near large roundabout. Walk a few paces then turn right onto a road. At

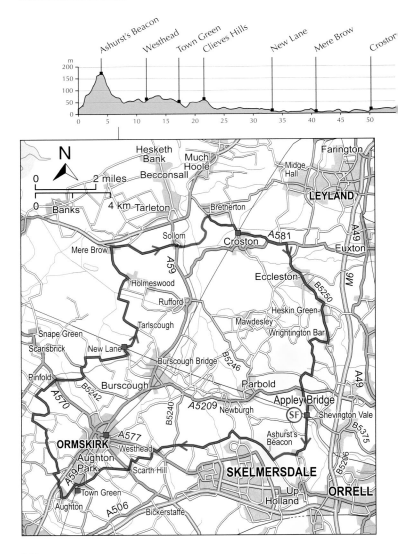

Wrightington Bar

0   65   70 km

a T junction turn right into Spa Lane and continue straight ahead.

At a crossroads by the Plough Inn go straight ahead into Dick's Lane. Turn right onto the **A577** then 1st left into School Lane. Go 1st right on Vicarage Lane, left on Wellfield Lane, then right and left on Scarth Hill Lane and past a prominent water-tower.

Cross the A570 and follow the road round to the right. After 2km go straight ahead at a crossroads. Meet the B5197 on the edge of Town Green, go left then right into Town Green Lane. Continue into **Aughton** and turn right at the village green. Go up to the A59. Cross over, turn right then immediately left on Mill Lane. At the end turn right on the B5195, then 1st left into Fir Tree Lane. Keep straight ahead for 3km through Clieves Hills.

At 'Give Way' sign on a bend turn right, then next right again into Asmall Lane. At the end turn left into Northmoor Lane, then next right just before a canal bridge. Go right at T junction into Morris Lane. Cross the **A570** into Smithy Lane and follow to T junction with the **B5242**. Turn left, over the canal, then 1st right on Drummersdale Lane.

Turn right on Merscar Lane. At a T junction turn left into **New Lane** and pass the station. At next T junction turn left on Fish Lane. Pass the Wildfowl and Wetlands Trust Centre at Martin Mere and continue to a T junction with the B5246. Go left to **Mere Brow** and turn right on a sharp left bend into Mere Brow Lane. After about 1km turn right on Green Lane.

Follow this to the **A59**. Go straight across into **Sollom**, turn left then right. Cross over the canal then fork left onto a newly-surfaced lane. Continue over Red Bridge. At a T junction turn right, then right again on Back Lane. At a T junction with the B5249, turn right.

After a railway bridge by **Croston** station turn left into Moor Road. Keep straight ahead, joining the **A581**, then turn right on New Lane, signposted Eccleston. At a T junction turn right on the B5250. Follow it through **Eccleston** and **Heskin Green** to **Wrightington Bar**, then turn right into Church Lane. At a T junction turn left on Toogood Lane. At next T junction turn right and follow round to a crossroads on the A5209. Go straight ahead for the long descent into **Appley Bridge**.

DAY RIDE 14

Preston–Whalley

Start	Preston station SD 535 289
Finish	Whalley station SD 729 364
Distance	41.5km/25.8 miles
Total ascent	501m/1645ft
Ride	Moderately hilly
See also	Stage 11

The problem with this route is that travelling between Preston and Whalley entails changing trains at Blackburn, but this is no great hassle and it makes for a much better ride than the Preston–Blackburn version featured in the previous edition of this guide.

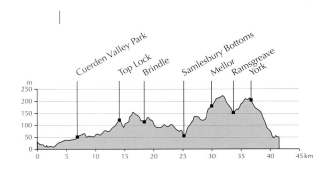

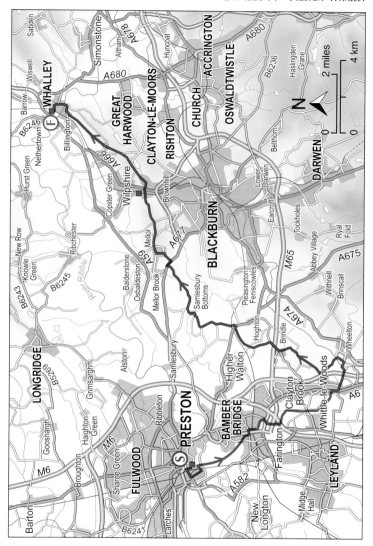

Preston station

The best exit from Preston station with bikes is via the lifts/ramps and subway towards the southern end of the platforms. Exit on Platform 7. Turn left through short-stay car park then left and left again to cross the bridge over the tracks. Descend through traffic lights, then turn left on West Cliff. At the end go straight ahead on a cycle track, under the railway and into Miller Park. Go under a bridge then follow the main cycle route, keeping high through Avenham Park, until you drop down to the Old Tram Road bridge.

Pick up NCN 55 signs and follow these for about 8km, riding through Cuerden Valley Park before exiting onto the **A6**. Turn right, then left down School Brow, left at the bottom, then right on Town Lane. Climb under the M61, up to a canal bridge at Johnson's Hillock Locks and continue up then turn left on Copthurst Lane and re-cross canal by Top Lock pub. Descend then climb to T junction and turn right. Descend into **Brindle** and turn right on the B5256. Cross over the M65 then turn left into Hillhouse Lane. Descend then turn right, signposted 'R C Church' and marked 'Private Road'. At the end, in **Hoghton**, turn right, then right again on the A675, then left into Gib Lane.

Take the next right, Goosefoot Lane. After 1km keep right then descend into **Samlesbury Bottoms** and climb out. Turn right into Further Lane and at the end turn right on the **A677**.

After 200m turn left and climb into **Mellor**. At a T junction turn right and climb steadily to ride along a ridge, then down to **Ramsgreave and Wilpshire** station and traffic lights. Go straight ahead and up Parsonage Rd. By a reservoir bear left on York Road. At the next T junction turn left. Descend through York village: beware speed bumps and hairpin at bottom. Turn right into **Whalley**. ▸

For the station continue past shops and turn left on Station Road.

DAY RIDE 15
Whalley–Longridge–Whalley

Start/finish	Whalley station SD 729 364
Distance	34.5km/21.4 miles
Total ascent	409m/1340ft
Ride	Moderately hilly
See also	Stage 4, Stage 3

A nice circuit: the first half, on the Cycleway route, is fairly gentle fare. The return leg over Longridge Fell is tougher but repays you with some excellent views.

Turn left out of the station to a mini-roundabout. Turn right, ride through **Whalley**, cross the River Calder and pass through **Billington**. Just past St Augustine's RC High School, turn right. Cross over the A59, ride through Old Langho and past the Black Bull pub, then turn right.

Continue to Ribchester Bridge. Join the B6245 to cross it. At **Ribchester** follow the road sharp right and

continue to **Longridge**. At top of a steeper climb, by the White Bull pub, turn right on Higher Road. Keep

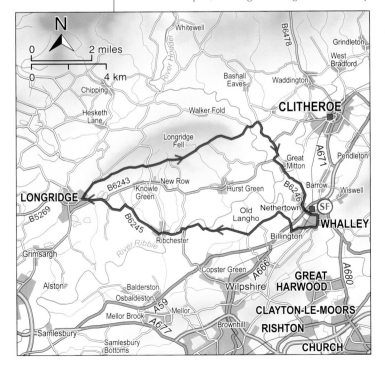

Early morning view from Birdy Brow, with Clitheroe in the middle ground

right at a fork and continue to a crossroads by the New Drop Inn (recommended). Keep straight ahead and follow road along flank of **Longridge Fell**, then descend Birdy Brow. ▶ At the bottom turn right and cross Higher Hodder Bridge. At the next crossroads turn right, re-joining the Cycleway route.

Turn right on the B6243. After 1km turn left onto the B6246. Ride through **Great Mitton** and on into **Whalley**.

There are great views along the fell but beware, the descent is steep.

DAY RIDE 16

Preston–Longridge–Woodplumpton–Preston

Start/finish	Preston station SD 535 289
Distance	50.4km/31.3 miles
Total ascent	264m/865ft
Ride	Gently hilly
See also	Stage 4, Stage 5

Earlier editions of this guide described this route as 'basically for the Cycleway completion fetishists though there's very pleasant riding once you're clear of the urban part'. The development of Preston's Guild Wheel, a 34km circular route, has greatly enhanced the urban part, too. This route utilises long sections of the Guild Wheel to start and finish: it is very well signposted and barely needs route description.

    The best exit from Preston station with bikes is via the lifts/ramps and subway towards the southern end of the platforms. Exit on Platform 7. Turn left through the short-stay car park, then turn left and left again to cross over the bridge over the tracks. Descend through traffic lights, then turn left on West Cliff. At the end go straight ahead on a cycle track, under the railway and into

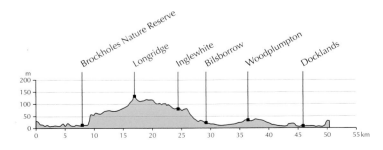

Miller Park. Drop down to a waymarked cycle route (the Guild Wheel) along river bank. Continue on the Guild Wheel, under the M6 to Brockholes Nature Reserve, and after short steep climb continue to meet B5269 in an industrial estate. ▶

There's a café at the nature reserve.

Leave Guild Wheel and turn right on B5269. Ride through **Grimsargh** and continue to **Longridge**. Bear right (almost straight on really) at a roundabout, and after a steady climb turn left down Berry Lane (with Tayah's café halfway down). At the bottom, turn right. Keep left by the Alston pub and follow a twisting road to and through **Inglewhite**. After another 1.5km, following a steep descent, keep left and continue into **Bilsborrow**.

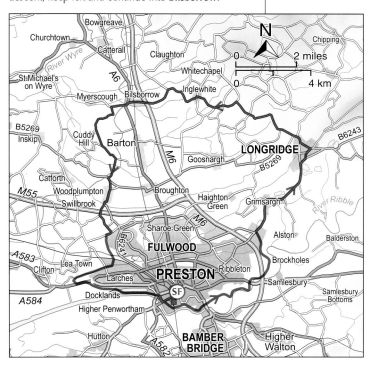

Turn left on the A6, then right on St Michael's Road. Take the 1st left (unsigned). Bear left at a T junction, then turn right, on a bend, on Hollowforth Lane. At T junction turn left on the B5269, then keep right on the B5411 through **Woodplumpton**.

After a bridge, where the B5411 swings left, take the minor road rising straight ahead. After a bridge over M55 keep straight ahead where the Cycleway turns right. At a T junction opposite a post office/newsagent, turn right for 200m then left on Miller Lane. At the end keep almost straight ahead, re-joining the Guild Wheel.

Follow this, with a section alongside the Ribble Link Canal.

Preston Docklands

The **Ribble Link Canal** was built as a millennium project and for the first time gave Preston, and the Lancaster Canal, a connection to the rest of the canal network. This entails a journey of almost 10km down the Ribble and up the mouth of the River Douglas to meet the Rufford branch of the Leeds and Liverpool at Tarleton Lock.

Later the route passes the Ribble Steam Railway (normally only open weekends and bank holidays) and the redeveloped Docklands area before completing the circle.

DAY RIDE 17
Kirkham–Lancaster

Start	Kirkham station SD 418 326
Finish	Lancaster station SD 472 617
Distance	71.7km/44.5 miles
Total ascent	404m/1325ft
Ride	Virtually flat to start, moderately hilly in the final third
See also	Stage 5, Stage 1a

This is both a longer distance than the other day rides, and a slightly awkward one as it requires a change of trains at Preston. However, the riding is mostly easy (particularly if you pick a day with a southerly breeze), and it fills an awkward gap for which no obvious alternative presents itself. Given the lack of serious climbing, it isn't really harder overall than some of the shorter but hillier stages. Pick the right day, give yourself plenty of time, have a few refreshment stops, and why not? But perhaps test yourself over a comparable distance with Day Ride 13 first. There are bail-out options too, notably heading to Poulton-le-Fylde station from Singleton or making a direct dash into Lancaster on the A588 or A6. A small toll (20p for bikes) is payable at Cartford Bridge.

From Kirkham station head for the town centre and bear left on Poulton St. Turn right on Freckleton Street, then cross the A583 at traffic lights. Follow a twisting road past industrial estates and an open prison before turning right into Hillock Lane. At a T junction turn right and continue into **Wrea Green**.

Keep straight ahead another 1.5km and cross the A583 at traffic lights. Cross over the railway, under the M55 then up to a T junction in **Weeton**. Turn left, re-cross the railway (take care at a narrow bridge) then after several twists turn right into Chain Lane and ride into **Staining**. Turn right on Mill Lane, just after the

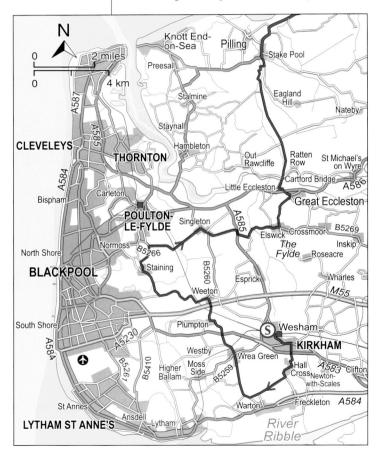

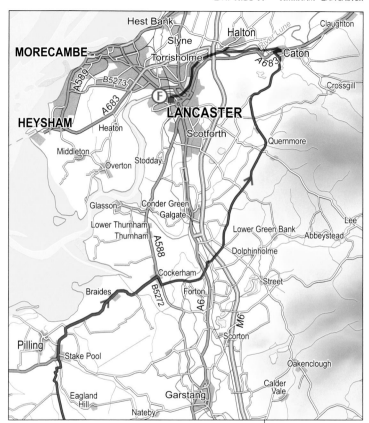

Plough Inn, then turn right on Smithy Lane, almost opposite a windmill.

At a T junction turn right on the **B5266** towards Singleton. At the next T junction, in **Singleton**, turn right again. After the Miller Arms pub, turn left on Mile Road (the B5269). After 2km cross the **A585**, continuing on theB5269 to **Elswick**, then turn left, signposted for Great

Cockerham

Eccleston. Climb through Copp into **Great Eccleston** and turn left at the T junction.

Continue to the A586, turn left then right into **Little Eccleston** (or cross the **A586** and use the cycle track). Descend to Cartford Bridge, pay the toll, turn right then turn left on Lancaster Road. Follow this for over 7km to meet the A588 at a T junction in **Stake Pool**. Turn right and continue to **Cockerham**.

Turn right on the **B5272**, then take the 1st left, Cockerham Rd. Follow this to the **A6**. Go straight ahead. After the Bay Horse Inn turn right, go under the railway, then left on Whams Lane.

Cross over the M6 and rise to a five-way junction. Go half-left, Bay Horse Rd, for a steady climb then long descent to the crossroads in **Quernmore**. Keep straight ahead and continue to a T junction, then turn right. Continue into **Caton**, then turn right on Copy Lane. At a T junction turn left to a mini-roundabout on the **A683**.

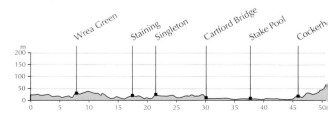

The Millennium Bridge

Go straight ahead, down a short lane, to meet a cycle path. Turn left and follow this to Crook O'Lune. Cross two bridges and continue to a small car-park by the old station building at **Halton**. Cross the lane and keep straight ahead, reversing Lancaster Link, under the M6 and alongside River Lune.

After the underpass continue past the Millennium Bridge and away from river. Meeting a street, turn right under the railway then left across a field to the station.

183

APPENDIX A
Further information

Tourist Information Centres
Centres on or close to the route are:

The Council Shop
Fernlea Avenue
Barnoldswick, BB18 5DL
Tel: 01282 666704

Pendle Heritage Centre
Park Hill, Barrowford
Nelson, BB9 6JQ
Tel: 01282 677150

Platform Gallery and Information Centre
Station Road
Clitheroe, BB7 2JT
Tel: 01200 425566

Lancaster Visitor Information Centre
The Storey, Meeting House Lane
Lancaster, LA1 1TH
Tel: 01524 582394

County Information Centre
Broadway
Nelson BB9 9SJ
Tel: 01282 698533

County Information Centre
45 Moor Street
Ormskirk, L39 2AG
Tel: 01695 579062

Rossendale Visitor Information Stand
Rawtenstall Library
Queen's Square, Haslingden Road
Rawtenstall
Tel: 01706 234694

For visitor information on the web, including accommodation, start at www.visitlancashire.com. This acts as a portal to most of the individual districts within the county. Areas which maintain their own dedicated tourism websites include:

Blackpool:
www.visitblackpool.com

Fylde:
www.visitlythamstannes.co.uk

Ribble Valley:
www.visitribblevalley.co.uk

South Ribble:
www.visitsouthribble.gov.uk

West Lancashire:
www.westlancs.gov.uk/leisure-recreation/visit-west-lancashire.aspx

General information
For general information about cycling, support for all kinds of cyclists, insurance and a wide range of other services, the premier organisation is **Cycling UK** (formerly the Cyclists' Touring Club, or CTC). They're based at Parklands, Railton Road, Guildford, Surrey, GU2 9JX. Tel: 01483 238301: www.cyclinguk.org.

Sustrans is another organisation that does great work, having now developed over 10,000 miles of the National Cycle Network, linking quiet roads and byways with purpose-built routes. They're at 2 Cathedral Square, College Green, Bristol, BS1 5DD. Tel: 0117 9268893: www.sustrans.org.uk. This website includes maps of the entire NCN (www.sustrans.org.uk/ncn/map).

The **Environmental Transport Association** provides a cycle break-down/rescue service. If you also drive a car, they provide excellent breakdown cover but won't spend any of your money campaigning for more roads. They're at 68 High Street, Weybridge, Surrey, KT13 8RS. Tel: 0333 0001234: www.eta.co.uk.

The **Camping and Caravanning Club** is useful if – you guessed it – you want to camp. They're at Greenfields House, Westwood Way, Coventry, West Midlands, CV4 8JH. Tel (bookings): 024 76475426: www.campingand caravanningclub.co.uk.

The **Youth Hostels Association** has hostels on or near the route at Arnside and Slaidburn. They're based at Trevelyan House, Dimple Road, Matlock, Derbyshire, DE4 3YH. Freephone 0800 0191700: www.yha. org.uk.

Cycling books and websites

The best all-round introduction to the what, why, where and how of cycling is still *Richard's Bicycle Book* by the late Richard Ballantine, originally published in 1972. Later incarnations including *Richard's New Bicycle Book* (1987) and *Richard's 21st Century Bicycle Book* (2000) may look slicker and update the technicalities, but don't really improve on its cocktail of passion and common sense. All are now out of print but not hard to find second hand. I haven't found any current book which does the same job even half as well.

Unless you ride a vintage bike, none of these can now be relied on for detailed advice on maintenance and repairs. Standards in many key components such as pedals and gears change all too frequently. For up-to-date advice on looking after your bike(s), seek out the latest edition of *The Bike Book* from Haynes, ISBN: 9780857331182.

If you're on a pure road bike, there's also *Complete Road Bike Maintenance* by Guy Andrews, published by Bloomsbury Sport, ISBN: 9781408170939.

From general advice to bike reviews and race reports, covering every variety of bike, there's masses of info at www. bikeradar.com. However, precisely because there's so much there, it can be a bit hard to find exactly what you need to know. More road-centric – as the name suggests – and much easier to navigate, is www.road.cc.

APPENDIX B
Transport

Making connections

National Express coach services no longer carry bikes, other than folding bikes. Citylink buses state that boxed/bagged bikes will be carried 'subject to availability of accommodation'.

Trains aren't just more comfortable for you, they are more comfortable for your bike as well. However, you can't always turn up at your local station and expect to load your bike straight on to the first train, still less to be able to do so for all your onward connections. Space for bikes is strictly limited on most trains, and a reservation is strongly advised when the train operator allows it.

Since the privatisation of the British Rail network an array of different train companies runs services in the region, each with its own policy on carrying bicycles. The information below was correct at the time of writing, but is of course subject to change. It's a good idea to check, particularly when planning a journey that involves services run by more than one company.

The rail network

The backbone of the region's rail network is, of course, the West Coast Main Line. The principal long-distance services on this line are run by Virgin Trains and stop at Wigan (North Western), Preston and Lancaster. Wigan is closest to the Southern Loop, while Preston lies between the two. Lancaster is best of all, as the link to the Cycleway is both short and traffic-free (and described in detail in Stage 1a, the Lancaster Link). The principal services on this line connect Glasgow and London, but Lancaster has at least one or two direct trains per day to/from many other places, including Edinburgh, Birmingham, Bristol, Southampton, Brighton and even Penzance.

Reaching the 'official' hub of the Cycleway, at Whalley, from the West Coast Main Line, requires changing trains twice, at Preston and Blackburn. However, there are direct trains to Whalley from Manchester (Victoria), via Bolton and Blackburn (operated by Northern Rail). These also stop at Entwistle, which is handy for the Southern Loop.

Other lines within the region include:

- Barrow and Windermere–Manchester Piccadilly and Manchester Airport (operated by Transpennine Express). Barrow trains stop at Silverdale and Carnforth, both on the Northern Loop. All trains stop at Lancaster, Preston, and Chorley. Some trains stop at Leyland, Buckshaw Parkway or Adlington, all handy for the Southern Loop.
- Blackpool–Preston. Transpennine Express and Northern Rail both run

trains over this section, stopping at Kirkham, close to the Northern Loop.

- Preston–Colne (operated by Northern Rail) via Blackburn and Burnley. Colne and Brierfield are quite useful stops for the Northern Loop.
- Preston–Bradford and Leeds (operated by Northern Rail). Stops at Accrington and Burnley.
- Preston–Ormskirk–Liverpool. There are no through trains on this line. Preston–Ormskirk services are operated by Northern Rail, and stop at Croston, on the Southern Loop. There is no Sunday service. Liverpool–Ormskirk trains are operated by Merseyrail and stop at Town Green, on the Southern Loop.
- Preston–Wigan North Western– Liverpool (direct trains are operated by Northern Rail).
- Manchester Piccadilly or Victoria– Wigan Wallgate–Southport (operated by Northern Rail). Appley Bridge and New Lane are both on the Southern Loop.

Train operators

There are four relevant train operators:

Virgin Trains operate the principal services on the West Coast Main Line and are the key carrier from most other parts of the country. Bicycles can normally be carried on all services but reservations are essential. Cycle reservations must be made by phone (0344 556 5650) or in person at a booking office.

Transpennine Express also run longer-distance services (eg Manchester–Edinburgh or Glasgow)

as well as a number of local services. Their stated policy is 'a maximum of two cycles per train with a valid cycle reservation.' Reservations can be made at ticket offices or by calling 0845 6001674 Monday–Friday between 08:00 and 20:00.

Northern Rail have won awards as 'Cycling Champions' and even have a dedicated website page (www. northernrail.org/travel/cycling). On their trains you just turn up with your bike. Space is of course limited and it seems sensible to avoid peak times but I've never yet failed to get on the first train.

Merseyrail have also won awards for their support of cycling. Bikes are carried on a first-come first-served basis and they recommend you avoid peak times: see www.merseyrail.org/plan-your-journey/getting-to-our-stations/bike.

All the companies offer online booking (for bodies if not for bikes) through their websites or you can use a general booking site such as **TheTrainline**: www.thetrainline.com.

Tandems

Regular tandemists already know this, but there are particular problems about carrying tandems on trains. Transpennine Express, Northern Rail and Merseyrail all state that tandems cannot be carried. Virgin Trains will do so, at least on their Pendolino trains, but it's essential to get the latest information and to make reservations in advance.

APPENDIX C
Bike Shops

Cycle shops offering spare parts and/or servicing, on or near the route, include the following. I can't personally vouch for all of them, but I have excluded one or two which have either made a poor impression on me personally or have received large numbers of negative reports.

Shops are listed for the two loops separately, in geographical sequence corresponding to the way the loops are described. Shops in Clitheroe are described under the Northern Loop but are also close to points on the Southern.

Northern Loop
The Edge Cycleworks
2 Chapel St
Lancaster LA1 1NZ
tel 01524 840800
www.theedgecycleworks.com

Leisure Lakes Bikes
103–105 Penny St
Lancaster LA1 1XN
tel 01524 844389
www.leisurelakesbikes.com

Lakeland Cycles
3 Whin Drive, Bolton-le-Sands
Carnforth LA5 8DB
tel 01524 735465

Dyno-Start Cycle Centre
3 Scotland Rd
Carnforth LA5 9JY
tel 01524 732089
www.dynostart.com

Pedal Power
Waddington Rd
Clitheroe BB7 2HJ
tel 01200 422066
www.pedalpowerclitheroe.co.uk

The Green Jersey
Shawbridge Sawmill, Taylor St
Clitheroe BB7 1LY
tel 01200 427630
www.thegreenjersey.co.uk

The Fell Bike & Tri Superstore
Unit 5 Deanfield Drive
Link 59 Business Park, Clitheroe
tel 01254 658950
www.thefellbiketri.com

The Bike Magician
41 Marsden St
Kirkham PR4 2TD
tel 07725 742491
www.bikemagician.com

Fylde Cycles
93 Poulton Rd
Kirkham PR4 2AJ
tel 01772 685404
www.fyldecycles.co.uk

Southern Loop
Wicked Cycles
Unit 1, The Exchange Building
Spring Lane, Colne BB8 9BD
tel 01282 863089
www.wickedcycles.co.uk

Ossie's Bike Shop
94 Scotland Rd, Nelson
tel 01282 693396
www.ossiesbikeshop.co.uk

On Yer Bike Burnley
Queen Street, Queens Lancashire Way
Burnley BB11 1AT
tel 01282 438855
www.onyerbikeonline.com

Ride-On
213–15 Bacup Rd
Rawtenstall BB4 7PA
tel 01706 831101
www.rideon.co.uk

Green Machine Bike Shop
146a Lee Lane
Horwich, Bolton
tel 01204 696831
www.greenmachinebikeshop.co.uk

The Bike Cabin
Ropeway Arcade,
Coppull Enterprise Centre
Mill Lane, Coppull PR7 5BW
tel 07479188030
www.thebikecabin.com

Alan's Bikes
47–51 Wallgate
Wigan WN1 1BE
tel 01942 826598
www.alansbikes.com

Winstanley's Bikes
9 Martland Court, Fourmarts Rd
Wigan WN5 0LU
tel 01942 707646
www.winstanleysbikes.co.uk

The Bicycle Lounge
46–48 Moor St
Ormskirk L39 2AQ
tel 01695 577240
www.thebicyclelounge.co.uk

Jack Parker Cycles
64 Liverpool Rd N
Burscough, Ormskirk L40 4BY
tel 01704 892442
www.jackparkercyclesburscough.co.uk

Leisure Lakes Bikes
Mere Brow
Tarleton PR4 6JX
tel 01772 814990
www.leisurelakesbikes.com

Bill Nickson Cycles
57–61 Towngate
Leyland PR25 2FQ
tel 01772 422259
www.billnicksoncycles.co.uk

Paul Hewitt Cycles
17–19 Preston Rd
Leyland PR25 4NT
tel 01772 424773
www.hewittcycles.co.uk

Merlin Cycles
A4 Buckshaw Link
Ordnance Rd, Buckshaw Village
Chorley PR7 7EL
tel 01772 432431
www.merlincycles.com

Mobile services
Mobile Bike Services
(mainly Blackpool/Fylde area)
tel 01253 864116
or text 07903 188185
www.mobilebikeservices.co.uk

WheelyGoodBicycles
(mainly Chorley area)
tel 07789 915710
www.wheelygoodbicycles.co.uk

DOWNLOAD THE ROUTE
IN GPX FORMAT

All the routes in this guide are available for download from:

www.cicerone.co.uk/849/GPX

as GPX files. You should be able to load them into most formats of mobile device, whether GPS or smartphone.

When you go to this link, you will be asked for your email address and where you purchased the guide, and have the option to subscribe to the Cicerone e-newsletter.

www.cicerone.co.uk

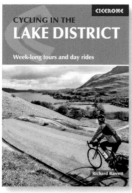
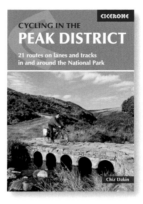
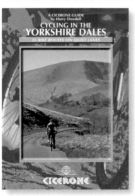

Walking – Trekking – Mountaineering – Climbing – Cycling

Over 40 years, Cicerone have built up an outstanding collection of over 300 guides, inspiring all sorts of amazing adventures.

 Every guide comes from extensive exploration and research by our expert authors, all with a passion for their subjects. They are frequently praised, endorsed and used by clubs, instructors and outdoor organisations.

All our titles can now be bought as **e-books**, **ePubs** and **Kindle** files and we also have an online magazine – **Cicerone Extra** – with features to help cyclists, climbers, walkers and trekkers choose their next adventure, at home or abroad.

Our website shows any **new information** we've had in since a book was published. Please do let us know if you find anything has changed, so that we can publish the latest details. On our **website** you'll also find great ideas and lots of detailed information about what's inside every guide and you can buy **individual routes** from many of them online.

It's easy to keep in touch with what's going on at Cicerone by getting our monthly **free e-newsletter**, which is full of offers, competitions, up-to-date information and topical articles. You can subscribe on our home page and also follow us on **Facebook** and **Twitter** or dip into our **blog**.

Cicerone – the very best guides for exploring the world.

CICERONE

2 Police Square Milnthorpe Cumbria LA7 7PY
Tel: 015395 62069 info@cicerone.co.uk
www.cicerone.co.uk and **www.cicerone-extra.com**